My 36 Years in Space

An Astronautical Engineer's Journey through the Triumphs and Tragedies of America's Space Programs

Kurth Krause

2017

To Paula,

Kurth Krause

Dedication

To my four wonderful grandchildren of whom I am very proud:
- ➢ Rachel Krause
- ➢ Karissa Krause
- ➢ Taylor Gildea
- ➢ Griffin Gildea

Acknowledgements

First I thank my wife Sue for her help in writing this book and for her support. I thank Bob Gildea, Taylor and Griffin's other Grandfather, who used his special engineering and grammar skills to offer corrections to the text. I also thank Richard Kallmann, my childhood friend, who used his eagle eye to proofread it. Dotty and Charlie Duke helped to rectify my memory of our life among the astronauts. I offer a special acknowledgement to Taylor, who used her graphic arts skills to design the cover of the book.

Most of the images were scanned from memorabilia I received over my career. Others were taken from NASA and military web sites. I acknowledge NASA, the US Military, and STSci as the sources for these images. Badger Boys State's website is the source of their "notable alumni." NASA Administrator Dan Goldin gave permission to publish his letters to me. The US Space Command allowed me to use its logo.

Contents

Preface 1

1. Why Space? 3

2. Astronomy 9

3. Graduate School—A Wasted Year 15

4. Titan III 21

5. Opportunity Knocks 26

6. A Whole New World 28

7. My Apollo Software 31

8. Apollo 1 42

9. El Lago—A Special Neighborhood 47

10. To The Moon from Woodland Drive 51

11. The Complete Apollo Mission 58

12. First Management Role 64

13. The Incomparable John Norton 69

14. Launch of Apollo 11 76

15. The First Lunar Landing 85

16. Apollo 12—The Luster Begins to Fade 95

17. The Most Successful Failure 99

18. Corrective Action 105

19. "Goodbye, Mr. Duke" 111

20. Apollo 17—The End of an Era 119

21. After Apollo 124

22. Space Shuttle Program—The Competitive Phase 129

23. Strategic Missile Defense 137

24. *Security Clearance—Serious, Not Glamorous* 142

25. *Ultrasystems* 151

26. *The Business Side of Aerospace–Not Dull* 154

27. *Intermetrics* 156

28. *The Space Shuttle—Operational Phase* 161

29. *GPS—Much More Than Military* 172

30. *Sy Rubenstein* 179

31. *Columbia—Search for a Scapegoat* 187

32. *Fired!* 196

33. *Job Search—A Campaign* 205

34. *Saving Aerojet* 214

35. *Burnout* 228

36. *Fighting Terrorism* 235

Epilog 240

Acronyms and Abbreviations 242

Preface

I wrote this book to give my grandchildren some insight into my chosen career of enabling and supporting space travel, exploration, and exploitation. It provides some historical, yet personal perspectives on the United States' pioneering into man's last frontier, and how it affected me. Although resembling a memoir, it focuses on my career, and not the many other aspects of my life. That may be another book: *"Choices—a Roadmap through Life."*

As a preteen in the early 1950s, the stories and "sightings" of flying saucers (or Unidentified Flying Objects as our government referred to them) fascinated me. In high school I decided to write a paper on the subject (which I still have). I researched the material thoroughly, reading every book and magazine article I could find on UFOs, and completed my paper, *"Flying Saucers—Fact or Fiction?"* with references from these publications. My paper did conclude the reality of UFOs and the likelihood of extraterrestrial beings piloting them (conclusions I no longer hold). But this helped to interest me in space travel.

I began reading and enjoying science fiction novels that dealt with humans (and other creatures) in space. But it all got real for me as a senior in high school when the Soviet Union successfully launched the artificial satellite, *Sputnik*. This small metal sphere traveled in a low earth orbit above the atmosphere at 17,700 miles per hour, reappearing every ninety-six minutes. This amazing accomplishment fascinated the world. It woke up our national leaders and triggered the beginning of the space age and our race with the Soviet Union. In July 1958, shortly after I graduated from high school, Congress passed the "Space Act," creating the National Aeronautics and Space

1

Administration (NASA). I recognized the profound significance of "the last frontier."

I have tried to minimize technical material; I don't want your eyes to glaze over. But I believe it's necessary to include some discussion of the math and science in order to convey an understanding of some important aspects of orbital mechanics and 1960s computer technology (Chapters 2 and 7). I have tried to use layman terms and avoid technical jargon so you don't need a course in celestial mechanics or advanced calculus in order to understand it. I have also converted measurements to US Customary Units (e.g., miles, rather than kilometers) to present it in familiar terms.

Although the material is presented primarily in chronological order, a few chapters depart from this and stand alone in order to dedicate them to colleagues who, in my opinion, occupy a special place among pioneers in the space field.

1. *Why Space?*

I wish I could say it was a calling. That it was in my blood. That the burning desire to be a "rocket scientist" consumed my every waking hour. I wish I could say that I fought all external forces that would have inhibited my quest, as in *"The Impossible Dream."* That would be glamorous. That would be a great story. But my decision to go into the space field actually comprised a series of events, interests, opportunities, and circumstances that led me to my profession. Most of us are not in full control of choosing a career. In actuality, our experiences guide us as much as inspiration. The great ones, maybe the lucky ones, seem driven to their goals by internal forces, rather than by their environment.

In retrospect, several events impacted defining my career path. In fact, possibly if any one of them had not happened, I might have become a teacher, a chemist, a doctor, an accountant, an actuary, or a mechanical engineer.

The most significant of these events occurred in the beginning of my senior year in high school when, on October 4, 1957, the USSR successfully launched *Sputnik*—the world's first artificial satellite—into orbit. Another moon orbiting the earth? This fascinated me. I really didn't know enough about orbital mechanics to understand exactly how it could stay up there indefinitely—neither falling to earth nor going off into space, but staying in an elliptical orbit around the earth. Its closest altitude (perigee) was 134 miles and its farthest point (apogee) was 584 miles above the earth's surface. Its orbit was inclined 65 degrees to the equator because it was launched directly from the Soviet Union's latitude. I had just begun learning about forces in my high-school physics course. I recognized the analogy with centripetal force—the force pulling inward to keep a ball on a string revolving around a fulcrum, rather than spinning off in a straight line. But this was different. I understood that it was gravity that was holding the satellite in its orbit. But I did not understand that the velocity of the satellite was exactly the speed necessary to offset the gravitational pull and bend it around the earth in a perfectly balanced trajectory, such that it would neither drift off in space nor fall to earth. It was in perpetual freefall (not zero G, nor escaping earth's gravity, as some reporters would mistakenly claim). Later, I would learn the derivation of Kepler's equation which approximated all trajectories in space.

Although this was the middle of the cold war, I was less interested in the military concerns that the Soviets would conquer space or that they had demonstrated capability to launch a missile at the US from 6,000 miles away. Instead, I marveled at the science of it. The fact that this primitive 184-pound twenty-three-inch sphere could do nothing other than send its "beep-beep-beep" signal, via its four radio antennae, back to earth also meant little to me. The signals continued for twenty-one days until its batteries died. But it stayed in orbit for three months until atmospheric drag eventually caused it to burn up in the earth's atmosphere as it descended. But this single event launched the US-Soviet Space Race, both to maintain parity in military capability and to gain the prestige of exploring space as the last frontier. And, although not fully cognizant of it, I had begun my preparation in being a part of it.

It's hard to reflect back to those days now. When I was growing up, there were no space programs, no astronauts, no satellites beaming data and multi-media communications to TV antennas or cell phones, no sophisticated flight computers, no spy satellites, and no launch vehicles to deliver intercontinental nuclear weapons. There was no NASA, no military space agency, and no major line items in the national budget for development of space assets. Sure, there were some pioneering efforts in rocketry. In the 1920s Robert Goddard successfully demonstrated how rockets that carried their own oxidizer with the fuel could propel a payload an indeterminate distance

4

because it did not require the oxygen present in our atmosphere to burn the propellant. Werner Von Braun and a team of scientists in the 1940s took this another step in developing the inaccurate, but terrifying, V2 rocket at Peenemünde Germany, launching bombs to wreak havoc on London in the final phases of World War II. But these were almost as primitive in power and accuracy as the Wright Brothers' first planes compared to today's aircraft. Both necessitated significantly more sophisticated automatic systems to navigate, target, guide, and control the launch vehicles and to process the data collected by payload sensors. This required much smaller and more sophisticated computers that could survive the rigors of space flight. The United States needed a great deal of development in launch vehicles, flight computers and software, and practical payloads. But the country had a real shortage of people with the right math and science backgrounds to carry out this development. No integrated college curricula satisfied this requirement. Computer science, space science, and missile engineering curricula did not yet exist. The US fiercely competed with the Soviets to recruit (capture?) the German Peenemünde team in an effort to partially fill this need. But fundamental math and science backgrounds in the schools suddenly became more important.

I guess the first event responsible for launching me on the road to prepare for a career in math and science began in third grade in the West Allis (suburb of Milwaukee) school system. I had earned only B's and few A's in first and second grade, perhaps because I disliked the teachers. My dad set some incentives: one dollar for each A and fifty cents for each B. I liked and respected my third grade teacher and she liked me. I started improving dramatically. When I came home with six A's and one B on my report card, my dad had to change the rules, since he could not afford to pay me. In 1948, that was a lot of money for an eight-year-old. (To put it in perspective, we bought our first house, a large two-story, in West Allis four years earlier for $8,000.) But more important to me was the praise I received from my parents and my teacher. I enjoyed the strokes from my teacher and parents so much that, from that point on, I always strived for top grades—a turning point in my education.

I continued to do well academically, and was the first in our family to graduate from high school. I missed achieving valedictorian and graduated with a 3.93 grade point. My only B's came from American History, where I disliked the teacher, but not the subject matter. Math and science were especially interesting and easy for me. I did have trouble with algebra the first few weeks. But then an excellent teacher, Ms. Mannix, worked with me until it clicked. To this day I use algebra as a problem-solving tool. I did not excel in reading and tended to read everything at the same pace in which I read a math or science text … probably because I analyzed each sentence for fear of missing something important hidden in the words. I scored in the 99th percentile in math and 60th percentile in reading on the National Merit Scholarship exam—good enough for a small National Merit Scholarship, one of three scholarships I won to attend the University of Wisconsin in Madison. I needed all three, plus the earnings from summer jobs, since my parents, although encouraging me, could not afford to pay anything toward college.

I saw myself as a bit of a geek in high school—small (5 feet 8 inches, 120 pounds with a twenty-eight inch waist as a senior). I did not do well at sports. I played baseball and basketball, but earned only a minor letter in baseball. However, I hung around with the jocks; my best friend, Richard Kallmann was a star basketball player. I earned my major letter by working as the head equipment manager (read "water boy") for our five football teams and 200 uniforms. I was Sports Editor of the weekly school paper and loved it. I dated several popular girls, but didn't make it into the "elite" clique. I guess I didn't see my true potential until I started winning many awards and scholarships as a senior, including earning an appointment to Badger

Boy's State, to Pen and Quill, and took second in the Milwaukee Elks Club's Most Valuable Student Contest. I actually placed higher than Al Jarreau, destined to become a famous jazz singer, who took third. Al had been president of his class since seventh grade, and achieved the all-city basketball team with the prettiest jump shot you ever saw. He was elected Governor of Badger Boy's State beating out Dan Travanti (who won two Emmys and a Golden Globe award in the 1980s for his role as Captain Furillo in *"Hill Street Blues"*). Al clearly deserved to win the Elks Club award, and probably didn't because he was black, from a black high school (Milwaukee's Lincoln High), and this was 1958. Jarreau earned his BS in psychology in 1962 and has won seven Grammys as a jazz and pop singer.

All the awards that I earned and the scholarships I won did help my self-esteem. Was I finally graduating from geekdom?

Although nothing in my course-work directly related to space, it did provide me with an excellent foundation for college. But neither my high school advisors, nor I, knew it would lead to the space field, since it did not exist at the time. When I told my high school advisor that I wanted a career to utilize math and science, he insisted that only teaching and engineering qualified. I chose mechanical engineering as a major, since I knew least about it. At that time my thirst for knowledge blazed a trail that was to see me through my first three years of college.

When I entered college, I felt scared. Sure, I did great in high school, but so did most of the 18,000 undergraduates enrolled at Wisconsin in 1958. I passed a math screening test to skip right to calculus, and in my first semester signed up for eighteen credits and thirty-two class-hours. They told us in Freshmen Lectures Class that two-thirds of us would flunk or drop out by our sophomore year. Fear of failure, my solid high school math, chemistry, and English background, and my sincere desire to learn, all contributed to a good start in college. I

7

worked hard my first semester, and obtained a 3.5 GPA. That earned induction into the honorary fraternity Phi Eta Sigma. I scored a 97 percent on the calculus final and learned enough to make the next two semesters of differential and integral calculus easy A's. The still new field of computer science warranted only one offering of an undergraduate class in programming at UW. The course introduced me to numerical analysis in addition to computers and software development. I loved it. This knowledge proved critical for in my work over the next ten years.

While the academics were the expected normal experiences leading to the space field, some unusual events also contributed to this career path. I remember as a child sometimes lying in the front lawn of our house in Milwaukee, looking at the sky and clouds and daydreaming of unusual things: the beauty of the sky and clouds, the space beyond, the universe, eternity. I was fascinated with the planets and their moons and especially our own moon. Sometimes I would fantasize that the world was a stage and everyone except me was an actor in a play, acting out their scripts for my benefit (or detriment, I wasn't sure which). I knew others would find it a little weird to think that way, but I could almost convince myself that it was true. I never told anyone until 1998, when I saw a similar plot in a movie called *"The Truman Show."* It brought back the memories of this fantasy, and I wondered if it were another event that helped to shape my chosen career path.

2. *Astronomy*

My first elective college course had the greatest impact on my career choice, although I didn't completely recognize it at the time. In February 1959 as I began the second semester of my freshman year at the University of Wisconsin, I finally had room to add an elective, and chose astronomy. The planets, moon, and stars had always fascinated me, but I had no idea how much more enjoyable it could be with the knowledge I gained in this class. Although the course had no firm prerequisites, the instructor did recommend a calculus background. Fortunately I'd completed one semester of differential calculus my first semester. Because of my A in calc I anticipated an easy course. I was wrong.

I found the course challenging, fun, eye opening, and stimulating. Some seniors took the course as a lark, thinking they'd get an easy three credits. They were wrong too. The professor, a real expert, loved his subject and excelled in the technology and the history of astronomy—not just the science. And he used calculus and other applied mathematics to help us understand the fundamentals.

The history fascinated me. The brilliant and insightful sixteenth century astronomers bravely opposed the "wisdom" of the times. They hypothesized models of the solar system, first from observation, then from theory, eventually changing what the world believed about the laws of the universe. Previously the religion-dominated thinking had insisted that the earth was the center of the universe, and the sun, stars and planets revolved around it. Copernicus, one of the very early astronomers, hypothesized in 1510 that the planets revolved around the sun and the earth rotated on its axis. This was a much simpler explanation as to why, for example, during certain times of the year Mars, Jupiter, Saturn, and Neptune appeared to reverse directions in migrating across the sky. Galileo hypothesized from observations, using the telescope he built, how the planets moved in nearly circular

9

orbits around the sun. He discovered the four largest of Jupiter's moons orbiting the planet and used their motion to determine his longitude at sea. I felt excited to observe these Galilean Satellites myself fifteen years later, when I bought a crude telescope for my children to see them orbit Jupiter in the Texas sky. Most people don't realize that they can see these four satellites with binoculars if they can hold them steady.

Kepler took Galileo's observations a step further, formulating Kepler's three laws of planetary motion—a model of the mutual gravitational attraction of any two masses, assuming all the mass of each is concentrated at the center of the body (a point mass). Gravity as such had not yet been completely understood, not even by Galileo or Kepler, although both contributed to its understanding. But Kepler's Laws enabled Newton to put it all together in describing gravity in a complete mathematical theory. Point masses are good approximations to the sun and the planets if the distribution of the mass of each body is spherically concentric. The earth's spin causes the radius at the equator (and therefore its mass) to be fourteen miles larger than at the poles, thereby introducing error in this approximation. Other forces, such as atmospheric drag, solar radiation pressure, and collisions with dust particles introduce additional errors in Kepler's laws, but they are nevertheless good approximations to the motion of one small celestial body relative to its much larger neighbor, such as the earth's motion around the sun. When the mass of one body dominates, the smaller will approximate a conic trajectory around the larger one. If the smaller is in orbit around the larger, it will approximate an ellipse with the larger body at one of the foci of the ellipse. A circle is just a special case of the ellipse, when both foci coincide. If the smaller body has sufficient velocity to just barely escape the gravitational attraction of the larger (escape velocity), the conic will be a parabola. If the velocity exceeds escape velocity, the conic will be a hyperbola. Kepler's laws resulted in three different equations to represent these three conics. The "universal parameter" allowing all three to be mathematically represented with the same equation had not yet been discovered. This discovery was to be critical in my contribution to the Apollo Space Program six years later.

So, for the first time, I could really understand the *Sputnik*. It could orbit the earth without power, free falling in an ever-curving trajectory around the earth, with sufficient velocity to sustain its balance with the gravitational force of the earth as long as solar radiation and collisions with gases and space dust did not significantly impede its elliptical orbit.

The major telescope we used was the most important and certainly the most glamorous part of the course. The University of Wisconsin had its own telescope on the top of beautiful Bascom Hill, the highest spot on the campus, just a few hundred yards from Lake Mendota—at that time, one of the largest refractor telescopes in the world with an 11.7-inch lens. Refracting telescopes differ from the large mirrored reflectors (such as Palomar) in that light passes through the lens to the eyepiece, rather than being reflected up to the eyepiece by a large mirror. So one does not have to climb up to the top to look down at the mirror, but can look directly up through the domed opening through the lens to the sky. We had night labs, where we peered through the telescope to see wondrous things:

- mountains and craters on the moon
- rings of Saturn
- moons of Jupiter
- spiral galaxies
- star clusters

How exciting (and difficult to accept) that all of these objects were not illusions. Pictures and textbooks could not provide the same feeling that came from their vivid presence. This was not abstract.

They were real! This was prior to the movies of *2001—A Space Odyssey* and *Star Wars*. But today these phenomena do not give me the same thrill as seeing these impossible, wonderful, majestic celestial bodies firsthand in real time. I would understand considerably more about them as my career took off. They never became mundane or jaded, but always exhilarating.

We have learned enormously more about our universe than when I took that class as a freshman in 1959, thanks primarily to the Hubble telescope, but also due to NASA's manned and unmanned explorations of the planets and the moon.

In 1959, we learned about only four galaxies, including our own Milky Way. Now we know more than 100 billion galaxies exist, each with billions of stars. One galaxy is believed to contain 100 trillion stars! We now know about black holes (depicted in image on right), where the gravity strength prohibits light from escaping. Our Milky Way has a black hole at its center with mass four million times greater than our own sun.

We've gained knowledge about nebula, gas and dust clouds from which form new stars and planets. Some stars have exploded, spewing matter radiating in all directions, forming supernovas. We learn about white dwarfs, dark matter, dark energy, gravitational waves, and red giant stars. Of course many of these phenomenal forms are billions of light years away. (A light year is the distance light travels in a year.) This means we see these bodies as they existed billions of years ago, not long

12

after the Big Bang, because it takes that long for their light to reach us. Look at the Hubble pictures of some spectacular nebula (http://hubblesite.org/gallery/album/nebula/) and tell me they are not fascinating.

But the study of our own planetary solar system is equally fascinating. From our manned and unmanned explorations we learned about the formation of our earth. Perhaps the most interesting fact: only earth has visible water, and lots of it. Most scientists believe that all the inner planets had some surface water at one time, but lost it due to absence of a strong atmosphere and/or the electromagnetic waves that protect us from the sun's radiation bombardments. Signs indicate that Mars and Neptune still have some subterranean water. Ice covers Mars' polar caps. Europa, the smallest of Jupiter's four Galilean satellites (slightly smaller than our moon), has more subterranean water than the earth's oceans. Water, of course, is necessary for the creation and sustainment of life as we know it, which is why, so far, we don't know of life on other planets in our solar system. But how did we get our water? When the earth was formed some 4.5 billion years ago, we may have not had surface water. Scientists presented several theories, including volcanic release of internal water vapor and water-laden meteors and asteroids colliding with the earth billions of years ago.

We now know that Saturn is not the only planet with rings (eight of them). Jupiter has three rings, Neptune has four, and Uranus has thirteen, but none as pronounced as Saturn's two major rings. We've known about Mars' two moons for some time, but now know that Neptune has fourteen natural satellites, Uranus has twenty-seven, Saturn sixty-two, and Jupiter sixty-seven! Perhaps more fascinating: Uranus lies on its side, rotating with its pole in the plane of its motion around the sun; Venus actually rotates backwards (clockwise). Experts think these unusual planetary rotations were due to large collisions with other heavenly bodies that knocked them off their normal axes. Similarly scientists theorize that our moon was formed four billion years ago when a collision with a molten earth ejected it. This is consistent with its composition as discovered from the Apollo moon rocks. But other bodies in our solar system are also fascinating. Between Mars and Jupiter lay millions of tiny minor "planets," labeled the asteroid belt. The largest of these, Ceres, is 572 miles in diameter and contains water vapor. But more than twenty-five million are smaller than sixty feet in diameter. The Kuiper belt that lies beyond Neptune also contains hundreds of thousands of "minor planets," the largest of which is Pluto

Astronomers theorize that the Big Bang formed our universe some fourteen billion years ago. All the mass, concentrated in a gravitational singularity, exploded. Our observations of the expanding universe (all bodies are receding from each other at velocities proportional to their distances apart) support this theory. This is also consistent with Einstein's theory of relativity. I accept this. I do not think this contradicts Genesis in how God formed the earth, moon, sun, and stars. I believe He created the universe via the Big Bang. Much of Genesis is also consistent with the chronology in the formation: first the planet Earth, then the water, then life.

Equally fascinating is the fact that we on earth are not stationary. Earth is spinning at 1040 mph at the equator, so at latitude 45° north we are moving at 750 mph. Add the speed of our planet around the sun: 63,000 mph. And our sun is moving through the Milky Way galaxy toward the star Vega at 45,000 mph. Then our galaxy is spinning, causing our sun to rotate around the center of the galaxy at 483,000 mph. Finally, our galaxy is moving away from the Big Bang at 1.3 million mph! We are indeed amazing space travelers through the universe.

All this stimulated my early interest in space, and is only reinforced as we learn more through exploration and observation.

3. *Graduate School—A Wasted Year*

In my junior year I finally qualified to take the advanced physics courses of advanced mechanics, optics, quantum mechanics, and atomic physics because I'd completed the prerequisites of advanced math classes. Advanced classical mechanics, including some rudimentary celestial mechanics, was my favorite by far. The news of America's initiation into manned space, Alan Shepard's suborbital flight in 1961 and John Glenn's orbital flight in 1962 enhanced my interest.

But by my senior year, my intense love of learning declined and compromised my interests. I was president of my fraternity, Alpha Delta Phi, intensely dating the love of my life, Susan Firle (whom I met on the student train to the 1960 Rose Bowl), and I started playing the card game, bridge. Yet, I made the mistake of going on to graduate school to get a Master of Science degree in physics, a goal I had promised myself. I turned down a full ride scholarship and teaching assistantship at the University of Cincinnati in physics because my UW professors said an MS in physics at Cincinnati was no better than a BS at Wisconsin. So I accepted a full ride at UW as residence counselor for thirty freshmen, while enrolling for a master's in physics. I wasted a year. The only graduate course I enjoyed and studied was Space Science; also the only course I aced. Not until I took graduate courses in Astronautical Engineering at MIT two years later did I reacquire my desire to learn.

In retrospect, maybe the 1962-3 school year was not a complete waste. I did earn and save several thousand dollars, working at the defense division of General Motors in Milwaukee the summer after my graduation, and learned about the guidance system for the Titan II intercontinental ballistic missile. I received my first Department Of Defense clearance, which allowed me access to the secret documents on the classified Titan guidance system. (My previous summer jobs included selling magazines door-to-door, making $50 per week in commissions, and loading trucks for $2 per hour.) Sue and I had made plans to be married after graduate school and I would accept an offer to work at GM in Wisconsin where she was employed and all of our relatives lived.

But, attending graduate school did give me convenient access to corporate recruiters who visited the UW campus. As a result I easily obtained additional good job offers once I earned my degree. I thought this was normal. In reality, history would show that this was the pinnacle in the soon-to-come aerospace cycle of feast and famine. Throughout the 1960s, space program funding remained high, due primarily to the excitement created by the first Mercury Astronauts, the Apollo Program, and even cold war funding for Intercontinental Ballistic Missiles (ICBMs). The arms race with the Soviet Union was no less important to the US than the space race. In the early '60s the USSR clearly led in space and the US had grave concern about them passing us in the arms race as well. These national priorities were at their peak. Funding was plentiful for both fields, creating shortages of people qualified to implement the programs. Therefore a 22-year-old college graduate with Math and Physics degrees could be easily fooled by the job environment at the time.

I enjoyed the experience of interviewing with several companies and to learn more about the industry. In addition, I had to admit that I loved the ego boost it gave me to visit these companies at their expense and see what they might offer.

The college recruiters, sent by these companies to UW, also fed my ego. They loved my degree, the double major in math and physics, and the fact that I was enrolled in the master's program in physics. They seemed pleased with my grades—particularly in my core courses—and seemed interested in ME! I received invitations to visit seven companies:

- Military and Space Division of GM in Oak Creek, Wisconsin (suburban Milwaukee),

- Space Technology Laboratories (STL), a Division of TRW, in Redondo Beach, California,

- A medical research division of General Electric Corporation in Milwaukee,

- Applied Physics Laboratories (APL) at Johns Hopkins University in Silver Springs, Maryland,

- The Astronautics Division of General Dynamics (GD) in San Diego, California,

- Bell Aerospace in Buffalo, New York, and

- The Federal Systems Division of IBM in Gaithersburg, Maryland.

I loved the experience of boarding a plane, renting a car, driving to the plant, having lunch with management, and generally being treated like an important person at these interviews. After all, I had rarely been outside the state of Wisconsin previously.

I particularly remember boarding a Continental jet from Madison to San Diego (in the dead of winter) to interview with GD. With only a few passengers onboard, I received a lot of attention from the attractive flight attendant who served me free drinks and sat down in the seat next to me to hear about my upcoming interviewing adventure in

California. Although I found the attention flattering, I was engaged to be married and had no interest in anything other than pleasant conversation. GD put me up in a plush hotel, nicely decorated with California foliage. The next morning two Human Resource (HR) personnel met me for breakfast at the hotel and drove me to the plant, which had a beautiful campus and lobby. After the HR interview they took me to another with the hiring supervisor. What a shock to see the work environment contrast: more than one hundred engineers in an open area of row after row of adjacent desks (accurately called a bullpen). Even the supervisor did not have his own office and seemed unhappy with his job. No one appeared to enjoy themselves. Although I followed through with all the interviews, I doubted I would ever be happy working there, even in the outstanding setting of beautiful San Diego.

By contrast, another California company, Space Technology Laboratories did impress me. I had already interviewed with several other companies prior to visiting STL, south of Los Angeles, in early spring of 1963. Once again I felt in awe of the warm weather, palm trees, and general ambiance of southern California. Three first-line supervisors, called Section Heads conducted my interviews. I was impressed with their professionalism, intelligence, and enthusiasm for their work. I also liked their private offices with enclosed ceiling-to-floor walls, rather than open-spaced bullpens or cubicles. I asked where *I* would be working, "in the basement?" Surprisingly I learned I would share a large, enclosed, windowed office with one other engineer, located adjacent to the supervisor's office. Their boss, Department Manager Bob Page (later to be a TRW Vice President) took me to lunch at a posh local restaurant and expounded on the

18

virtues of STL, the work, and the LA living area in general. I returned to Madison wondering if Sue and I should consider changing our plans about Milwaukee and GM.

By late April the offers started arriving, and in early May I received solid job offers from each company, except APL. They ranged from a low of $650/month from IBM to a high of $721/month from STL. GM offered $685/month. I was angry that APL did not respond with their offer by the promised date of early May so that I could make my decision and give all companies an answer in time for them to meet their hiring goals. I called APL and told them I needed their offer now. They responded with a rejection letter. What a blow to my ego, since by now I was full of myself, puffed up by the previous six offers. So I did something stupid. I wrote APL about their inconsiderate response, making me wait three weeks beyond our agreed deadline to get their rejection, and I would report this to the UW Placement Center to warn others of APL's behavior. This prompted APL to contact UW directly to protect their interests and reputation on campus. This was my first lesson in letting my bruised ego get ahead of good judgment. I should have simply accepted their rejection and moved on like a professional.

Sue and I seriously discussed the possibility of forgoing our plans to accept the GM offer in Milwaukee and taking the STL job in California. (I soon learned Sue would always be adventurous.) But after several phone calls and much discussion, we decided to stick with our original plan. After finishing her Occupational Therapy internships, Sue was enjoying her new job as a registered OT on a pilot program in the psych ward at Milwaukee County Hospital. Also, we were reluctant to leave all our Wisconsin relatives. We concluded that if I later determined the GM position was not challenging enough, I could always re-apply at STL and we could take on the California adventure. I guess I was a brash, new hotshot who thought I could do anything I wanted. I was very naïve.

4. *Titan III*

Sue and I married on June 15, 1963 in Fond du Lac Wisconsin, her hometown. Fortunately, I had saved my earnings the prior summer, making the financial challenges to married life reasonable. We bought a new Volkswagen Beetle for $1,900 and new furniture for our apartment before driving to Door County for a one-week honeymoon. Although I told Sue we would never be wealthy, I felt flush as we planned to save her $5,000/year salary and live on mine. We moved into our new, tiny three-room apartment in Milwaukee, and I started work at the military and space division of GM the day after returning from our honeymoon.

I worked with a small team of engineers (most had advanced degrees) on the guidance system being developed for the new Titan III vehicle. It would launch various Air Force capsules into earth orbit. My immediate supervisor was Dr. Spencer Macy, the former head of the physics department at the South Dakota School of Mines. His boss, Dale Wilmoth, also earned his PhD in physics. I expected to learn much from them, but

didn't. I would be one of eight engineers working to verify, validate, and ensure that the Titan III guidance system software would fulfill its mission of inserting USAF payloads into their proper orbits in space. Martin Marietta in Denver developed a family of expendable rockets for the Air Force. The Titan II was the workhorse ICBM and also the launch vehicle for NASA's Gemini Program. GM had the contract for the guidance system. Titan III was to be used for launching military satellites, primarily from Vandenberg Air Force Base in California. I worked on the Titan III A, which was much like a Titan II with an upper stage (Transtage) capable of multiple burns.

GM built the Inertial Measurement Unit (IMU) and integrated it with an IBM flight computer to create the guidance system that we were to validate. Aerospace Corporation in El Segundo California designed the guidance algorithms for the flight computer. Both the guidance algorithms and the accuracy of the IMU had a SECRET classification because the accuracy of the related Titan II ICBMs could be easily inferred from the Titan III documents. Thus my clearance from the previous summer carried over, allowing me access to the classified documents on my first day at work.

Dr. Charles Stark Draper at the MIT Instrumentation Lab designed an inertial platform at the heart of the IMU. He was known as "The Father of Inertial Guidance." The platform is gimballed in three dimensions, so it can remain in a fixed orientation in inertial space, while the vehicle containing it rotates in all three directions of pitch, roll, and yaw. The three gimbals then precisely measure the degree of rotation from the inertial platform in order to measure the vehicle's (and its thrusting engine's) orientation in inertial space. Mounted on the platform are three mutually perpendicular accelerometers that measure the vehicle's acceleration in all three dimensions.

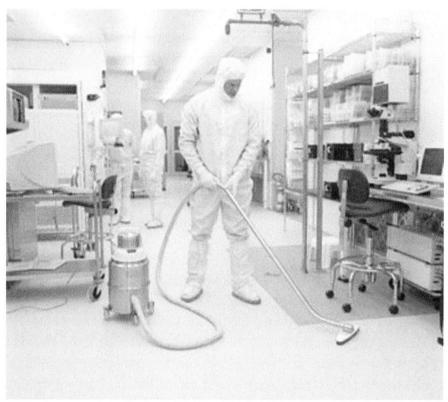

GM won the contract to build these because their IMU was the most accurate in the industry. Each gyro and accelerometer was built in a "Clean Room," in which all dust particles were sucked out preventing contamination which would degrade the precision of the components. People working in the Clean Room had to enter an antechamber to exhale dust from their lungs, blow all dust particles from their clothes, and don a clean suit, booties and hairnet before entering the Clean Room. Even with all these precautions, GM had to discard 90 percent of the components because they didn't meet the stringent accuracy requirements. Obviously the IMUs that passed the tests for integration into the Titan III Transtage were outrageously expensive.

However, our group's job was not to build any hardware, but rather to verify that the software would use the IMU measurements to navigate and guide the Transtage to its desired orbit, trajectory, or target. While the work was not exciting, it did present its challenges.

For example, one challenge was to launch a special payload, the USAF manned spaceplane X-20 Dyna-Soar ("Dynamic Soarer"), into various trajectories for surveillance, satellite intercept, and space rescue missions. It could be piloted to return to earth as a glider. Neil Armstrong was selected as one of the test pilots. The X-20 was a winged  payload on top of the Transtage, but it required a precise trajectory through the atmosphere to avoid breakup. One of my assignments was to create a polynomial curve to meet these requirements. To do this I used a least-squares curve-fit program on our large mainframe computer. But the results were unsatisfactory giving large deviation errors from the desired flight path. I was able to use my knowledge of numerical analysis from my college computer science course to prove to the programmers that their curve-fit software was inadequate and causing the large deviations. At first they didn't believe me, so I had to use a $2,100 Friden mechanical calculator to manually execute the matrix inversions required for the curve fit to show them they had to change the software to triple precision in order to avoid the loss of accuracy. (Note that this was 1963, and the ten dollar electronic calculators had not yet been invented.) Reprogramming the curve-fit software using triple precision made all the difference—the accuracy of my polynomial was perfect. Unfortunately, the Dyna-Soar Program was cancelled soon after my breakthrough. At the time, it was the most advanced manned space program of its kind. Not until 1981 did the Space Shuttle accomplished similar capabilities.

So I had to return to the tedium of the software verification work. I also amused myself with nontraditional work. I remember writing a paper in which I proved that if one used a coordinate system that was not centered in the earth, but rather in the sun, then the inertial platform **was not** an inertially-fixed orientation in sun-space. (Return of some geek tendencies.)

I did enjoy the occasional business trips to Southern California to meet with the designers of the software algorithms at Aerospace Corporation, a spinoff from STL. I traveled with my two bosses, Dr. Macy and Dr. Wilmoth, on planes that were far from full capacity because airlines fares were still subsidized by the government as a fledgling industry under development. A few years later these government supports and regulations were lifted and airlines had to fill their planes to make a profit. But at that time, air travel was great. Continental Airlines offered free meals, and they gave us two drinks and cigarettes between Milwaukee and Denver—then again between Denver and Los Angeles. Once when Wilmoth's boss went with them, he drank all six of their drinks on both legs. (Macy and Wilmoth did not drink.) They almost had to carry him off the plane. Macy and Wilmoth always stopped at a grocery store in LA to bring fresh California oranges home to Milwaukee.

My job got better when the Air force hoped to fly the Transtage to the moon. GM was designing a payload which would send back signals as it crashed into the moon to measure the depth of the lunar dust. This would be placed in the nose of the Transtage and released before impact. I flew to our Santa Barbara research facility to learn how to use a digital space simulation developed by our laboratory there. I used this digital simulation to design and test guidance algorithms enabling the flight computer to guide the Transtage to the moon.

5. *Opportunity Knocks*

Frank Rumreich, the senior engineer of our section, was in charge of developing the digital simulation of the Titan vehicle and its surrounding gravity and atmospheric environment. We used this simulation to test the guidance system software for the multitude of missions. Frank gave me some great advice when I complained of growing bored with the lulls in my job. Using my spare time at work to learn something new was about to pay off big time. My experience with the new lunar mission guidance and navigation algorithms on Titan III uniquely qualified me to fill a critical vacancy on the Apollo Program. Due to the accuracy of their gyros and accelerometers, GM won the NASA contract for the Apollo Guidance System. The Instrumentation Lab at the Massachusetts Institute of Technology (MIT/IL) had the NASA contract to design the two guidance flight computers for the Command Module (CM) and the Lunar Module (LM), the navigation hardware, and all the flight software. GM was to build the Inertial Measurement Unit and integrate all the components together into guidance systems for the CM and LM. The contract included having several employees on loan to MIT/IL in Cambridge, Massachusetts to assist in their critical engineering activities (MIT/IL did not want to go through the hiring and layoff cycles). One of these assignments involved working directly with the MIT flight software team. I was to fill this spot. But at the time, I did not really understand how important the opportunity would be and how it would shape my entire career.

It was September 1965, and I was a brash, twenty-five-year-old, know-it-all. Sue had given birth to our son, Scott, just three months prior and had quit her job as an occupational therapist to stay home and raise him. We had saved our money during our eighteen months of marriage and bought a new home in December 1964. We had just completed furnishing the home when the MIT opportunity popped up.

I had become bored with my job at GM ever since NASA had ordered the USAF to abandon their plans to use the Titan III to send an experimental payload crashing into the moon to test the surface hardness. Since this preceded NASA's first lunar probes, no one knew how many inches (or feet?) of fine dust might have to be penetrated before encountering a hard lunar surface for landing. Exploration of the moon was NASA's charter, and they certainly didn't want the Air Force to steal their thunder, even if they had the Titan III launch vehicle and Transtage to do so. Therefore my work on the guidance equations to steer the Transtage and its payload to the moon was ordered to stop. I had to go back to the mundane job of verifying that the Titan III flight software would successfully deliver the Air Force's satellites to a synchronous orbit. This was a circular orbit in the equatorial plane 23,000 miles from the earth's center, rotating with the earth directly over a single point on the equator.

I was considering whether to look for a better job, when GM offered me the opportunity to transfer to Massachusetts ... an easy decision, despite our new baby and new home. GM would pay for moving up to 2,000 pounds of belongings and also pay our expenses up to two weeks while we waited for housing. They allocated $150/month allowance to rent a home, and $100/month to rent furniture for the planned eighteen month stint. Sue and I were both looking for an adventure. We had never lived outside of Wisconsin and, as a family, had rarely even traveled outside the state. I had to interview for the job with the MIT staff, but I was confident I would be accepted. I could use my interview trip to look for housing. I was off to Boston.

6. *A Whole New World*

Renting a car and driving in Boston was a real challenge for someone from Wisconsin. The traffic, weird streets, discourteous drivers, unusual traffic laws, and strange environment actually frightened me. I stayed at the Statler Hilton Hotel in downtown Boston right across the Charles River Basin from the MIT Instrumentation Lab in Cambridge. I remember coming out of the hotel at 5:00 PM and staring with my mouth open, as I gawked at the cars triple parked in the four-lane no-parking zone in front of the hotel ... not a ticket on a single car, despite the police officer directing traffic and another walking along the illegally parked cars. *You're not in Wisconsin anymore, Kurth!*

My interviewer, Bill Marscher, a member of the MIT Lab staff was a tall, forty-something transplanted South Carolinian. Unlike the typical New Englander with a Boston accent, he had a charming southern drawl and easygoing manner. But I did notice the MIT ring he wore, announcing his MS in Astronautics. He was no redneck. I remember feeling a little insulted (naïve young engineer that I was) when Bill dwelt on my college courses and grade point average. Although proud of my academic record, I naïvely believed the **two whole years** of experience on the Titan III guidance system was much more relevant and spoke volumes about my capability. I assumed that the Lab's ties to MIT promoted this academic snobbery, since nearly everyone I met wore his MIT class ring. Dr. Charles Stark Draper, a notable figure on the MIT faculty, was the director of MIT/IL. (Draper had received the Presidential Medal of Freedom, the nation's highest award for civilians, for his work on inertial guidance.) Dr. Richard Battin, who headed the Apollo software project at the Lab, was also the chairman of the newly formed MIT Department of Aeronautics and Astronautics. Of the forty people within the Lab reporting to Battin, all but a handful had degrees from MIT, most of them doctorate or masters degrees. A few were graduate students in astronautics, one or two years away from completing the requirements for their doctorates. Marscher elaborated on the brilliance of each of these forty people. Bill explained that all members of the Instrumentation Lab staff could join the MIT faculty club (myself included). I got past my immature snit, and Bill seemed satisfied with my background. I was accepted as member of the staff and took off on the most exciting technical journey of my professional life.

The environment at the Lab was much more casual than in industry. The MIT academic culture had a big influence. We each had our own office, but with few niceties. The offices, actually open cubicles, were noisy and a bit dingy, with exposed ugly pipes running across the ceiling. But the Apollo building, MIT/IL-7 was on the bank of the Charles River Basin and across the way a spectacular view of downtown Boston. Except in winter, when the Charles froze over, the MIT and Harvard rowing teams would practice sculling on the Charles, the coxswains rhythmically barking out their cadences.

But the Apollo team worked like a tightknit family. I remember each of them vividly ... all interesting personalities. Several had unusual, British-like names, such as Bob Bairnsfather, Hugh Blair-Smith, and Alan Klump. And Marscher was right—each was brilliant in his field.

There was not much real organizational hierarchy at the Lab. Dr. Richard Battin was the titular head of our group of forty engineers responsible for developing all the flight software for the each of the Apollo flights. But, in reality, he did not manage us. He spent much of his time updating his newly published book, *Astronautical Guidance*, teaching his classes, and chairing international conferences in the field. And initially there was no real structure under Battin in the Lab. Rather than allocating responsibilities for developing different portions of the flight software via a hierarchy of managers, each of us decided what functions of the software we would develop, reaching a consensus between us. Marscher undertook the assignment of writing the backup software to guide the Saturn through its boost phase in case IBM's software in the Saturn computer failed. Marscher was to be my mentor.

7. *My Apollo Software*

As an inexperienced 25-year-old engineer, I was given an awesome responsibility to develop the Apollo flight software in September 1965. I did not appreciate the magnitude of the assignment, nor the unique privilege, until years later—well after the first landing on the moon. I was to develop the onboard program to be loaded into the CM and LM computers that would return the astronauts safely to earth from any point in their lunar mission trajectories. Not only had this never been done before, but also the proper targeting and guidance algorithms to steer the spacecraft had not yet been developed, let alone programmed into an onboard computer. Some textbook equations provided a basis for their development in theory, but they had never been put into practice.

I was accepted into graduate school at MIT in order to take Battin's new course on Astronautical Guidance concurrently while working ... a unique, ideal experience, applying almost daily to my job what I learned in class. Since no one had ever designed a return-to-earth program before, a totally new set of algorithms had to be developed to determine the correct state vector (position and velocity) from any point in the mission: earth orbit, lunar orbit, or any place between. Marscher had already begun to develop some ideas on how to make the computations, but nothing solid to date. In the next eighteen months, I was to develop the right algorithms, verify them on the Lab's large scientific computer (the Honeywell 1800), program them into the CM flight computer, and verify they would work for all possible mission situations. It would be fun, and I never doubted its success. I didn't realize at the time how little I knew ... how little any of us knew!

Early on, I started to learn about the two flight computers. The LM and CM flight computers were to be hardware-identical, each with its own unique software for targeting, guiding, and controlling its respective part of the mission. In addition, they would provide the necessary information for the crew to fulfill their duties.

The computer hardware dictated the worst of the practical constraints. This computer, designed by MIT/IL and built by Raytheon, was of 1960 technology:

- 20 instructions for adding, subtracting and moving data around (multiplication was performed via repetitive adds; division via repetitive subtractions)

- 16 bit word length (with one sign bit and one parity bit, leaving only 14 bits for data)

- Fixed-point arithmetic (meaning that one had to use software to ensure that each word of data was *always* of value less than 1.0; otherwise the data would "overflow" causing catastrophic results)

- Cycle time of 11.7 microseconds (The central processor in today's PC is forty thousand times faster!)

- Hard-wired memory (Read-Only Memory or ROM) of 36,864 words

- "Erasable" memory of 2,048 words (Today's PC equivalent may contain ten billion or more bytes of RAM!)

- Zero "mass storage" memory (Today's PCs have over one trillion of bytes of disk memory.)

- An asynchronous executive in which higher priority programs could interrupt and suspend lower priority ones, which would later resume when the higher priority ones had completed

When I tell new computer-science graduates about the Apollo flight computer, they stare at me in disbelief. Some blurt out the impossibility of having flown to the moon and back on two such computers, each with only 36,864 words of fixed memory. In today's age of computers, where our programs gobble up memory in megabytes, it is indeed hard to believe that such a feat was possible.

Because a computer had to be qualified to fly in space, each had to be radiation-hardened and highly reliable. A charged space particle could "zap" an unprotected processor or its memory and destroy a single word of data, jeopardizing the mission during a critical maneuver. Therefore, after the core rope memory was completed with the wires depicting the 1's and 0's required by the software, it was encapsulated in epoxy to protect against the radiation created by the sun. Since the memory had to be meticulously hand wired, bit by bit, before encapsulation, we had to freeze the software six months before each flight.

The most challenging of these constraints were the limited memory and the slowness of the computers. The guidance cycle had to complete its computations for a new command to the main engine every two seconds. The control cycle had to calculate its commands to the autopilot that fired the attitude control jets every forty milliseconds. Each of these constraints was a major challenge for every member of Battin's team: Jerry Levine – navigation, George Cherry and Alan Klump – Lunar Module, Margaret Hamilton – executive operating system, Ed Copps and Bob Bairnsfather – reentry, Bill Marscher – Saturn launch, Norm Sears and Fred Martin – integration, Don Frazer and Bill Widnall – simulation.[1]

How were we going to fit all our guidance, navigation, control, and auxiliary software into 36,864 words? First, under the leadership of Dr. Jim Miller, we built an interpreter, 2048 words of subroutines that would examine 107 powerful software pseudo instructions and translate them in real time into the twenty hardware instructions of the

---

[1] Bill's wife, Sheila, was appointed the first female Secretary of the USAF by Bill Clinton in 1993. She earned her doctorate in Aeronautics from MIT in 1964.

flight computer. In this way, we could command something as powerful as "double precision matrix times three-dimensional vector" in one word, which at run time would then invoke hundreds of machine language instructions to carry out the mathematics of this transformation of a vector. However, we paid a heavy tradeoff price: each interpretive instruction would carry a ½ millisecond overhead time penalty to unscramble the instruction and correctly carry out the sequence of hundreds of machine instructions.

My "Return to Earth" program was likely to be as complex as any on board. Therefore, the challenge of computing it fast enough and using a minimal portion of the 36,864 words would require a real breakthrough in algorithm development. After months of analysis, I concluded "Return to Earth" would require solving five different free-fall trajectory design problems:

1. Kepler's Problem: Given the initial position and velocity of the spacecraft, what would be its position and velocity at a given time in the future?

2. Lambert's Problem: Given the initial position of the spacecraft, what velocity must it have such that at a given time in the future it will arrive at a fixed point in space?

3. Time-Radius Problem: Given the initial position and velocity of the spacecraft, what would be its position and velocity when it reaches a given distance from the earth's (or moon's) center?

4. Time-Eccentric Anomaly Problem: Given the initial position and velocity of the spacecraft, what would be its position and velocity when it sweeps through a given angle centered at the earth (or moon)?

5. Reentry Problem: Given the initial position of the spacecraft, what velocity must it have such that it reaches earth's reentry altitude with a given reentry angle?

All of these problems could be solved using conic approximations to the real trajectories with great accuracy. If the earth were a perfect sphere whose density varied only with the radius from its center, its gravitational attraction could be represented as a point mass. If other heavenly bodies had a negligible gravitational attraction on the spacecraft, if solar radiation could be ignored, if there were no molecules of air or dust in space to cause drag, and if the spacecraft were in "free-fall" (coasting, not thrusting), then the spacecraft would travel in one of three perfect conic trajectories around earth:

1. **Ellipse** with one of the two foci at the center of the earth (A circle is just a special case of an ellipse with both foci at the same point.)

2. **Parabola** with the single focus at the center of the earth (The spacecraft would have just enough velocity to escape earth's gravity, coasting to infinity.)

3. **Hyperbola** with the focus at the center of the earth (The spacecraft would have more than enough energy to escape earth's gravity, having velocity left over when it reaches infinity.)

These three types of two-dimensional geometric shapes are called conics because they can be constructed from taking slices through a cone. Slicing off the top of a cone at an angle produces an ellipse. A slice perpendicular to the axis produces a circle. A slice parallel to the axis produces a parabola. A slice at an angle to the axis that does not cut off the top produces a hyperbola.

The same approximations and conic trajectories work with one of the foci at the center of the moon. The nominal trajectory design for a lunar mission requires that the spacecraft launch to an elliptical (nearly circular) earth orbit, then burn its main engines to coast into an almost parabolic trajectory to leave earth and traverse to the moon. As it approaches the moon and is predominately influenced by lunar gravity, it is in a hyperbolic trajectory with the moon's center as its focus. Then, the spacecraft does a retro burn to reduce its speed enough to enter an elliptical orbit around the moon. The LM, after it separates from the CSM, does a final retro burn to kill off the rest of its velocity in its descent to the moon. The ascent from the moon, rendezvous with the CSM, and return to earth repeat these free-fall (coasting) trajectories of ellipse, hyperbola (relative to the moon's center), and parabola (relative to the earth's center) approximations.

My Return-to-Earth program required each of these conic trajectories because it had to compute the return trajectory from any point in the mission. There were three modes:

1. Nominal: Return to a specific landing site (or in the case of Apollo, a designated splash-point in the ocean).

2. Fuel Critical: Return, burning the minimal amount of fuel.

3. Time Critical: Return in the shortest possible time.

The mathematical problem with dealing with each of these conic trajectories is that each required solving Kepler's equation for an object in free-fall in three different forms. Worse, as the elliptic and the hyperbolic forms approached the parabolic energy, they produced a mathematical singularity, causing one of the parameters to grow without bounds. Fortunately, both Battin and Dr. Sam Herrick had solved this problem by introducing a "universal variable." This variable, discovered only two years earlier, and now appearing in Battin's 1964 textbook *Astronautical Guidance,* enabled me to solve Kepler's equation with a single, universal form for all conics, making the singularity disappear.

But one major practical problem remained: in order to minimize the use of the precious read-only memory, I needed to find a way to integrate the solution of all five conic trajectory design problems. Bill Marscher discovered an algorithm that could be used as a kernel for solving both Kepler's problem and Lambert's problem. I was also able to extend it to the Time-Radius, Time-Eccentric Anomaly, and Reentry problems, but it introduced an unacceptable side effect. The resulting hyperbolic trigonometric transcendental equations could not be solved explicitly but, rather, required an iterative solution that used up more computation time than we could afford.

I began a labor of love to find a way to solve it explicitly. I loved applied mathematics in those days, often entertaining myself with deriving unusual equations and calculus integrals, rather than looking them up in math books. (I think they called mathematical geeks like us "purists.") After almost six months of trying several techniques, Bill Robertson and I finally found the solution. Bill was a recent graduate of Princeton's master's program in mathematics, and a joy to work with. We published the result in technical journals and I began to implement it into the flight computer software.

My thirst for knowledge was revived. I was impressed with the MIT professors, but even more impressed with the graduate students in my classes. They actually read ahead of the assigned material, reading much of the bibliography at the end of each chapter. I was convinced they were qualified to teach the classes.

I also started doodling with mathematics while waiting for my computer run to finish. At the lab we had no programmers. We even did our own keypunching, gave the deck of computer cards directly to the shift operator, and waited for the results. My math doodling included playing with Fibonacci numbers, infinite series, singularities, and deriving hyperbolic trig identities. It was fun! (OK, so maybe geeky.)

I digress here to repeat a joke about the early days when computers read punched cards into their memories to load the software programs. The person in charge of spacecraft weight interrogated everyone to determine their weight budgets for the flight. When he asked the programmer, his response was the weight budget should be zero! He went away bewildered and shaking his head. Later he came back with a deck of keypunched cards, showed them to the programmer and said this is a lot of weight! "No," the programmer said. "We just use the holes."

Around this time, the NASA management at the Manned Spacecraft Center (MSC) in Houston expressed concern about our keeping NASA insufficiently informed of our progress with the flight software. They were so right! We documented our algorithms only when we published technical papers. Christopher Columbus Kraft, then Director of MSC Flight Operations, held a series of Friday meetings at MIT/IL to determine the status. At one of these meetings (dubbed Black Friday) he learned that our sizing of the memory requirements for our programs was grossly inadequate. At the time, there were forty of us, each writing our portion of the flight software under virtually no supervision. (MIT people did not appreciate someone looking over our shoulders.) Kraft asked each of us how much memory we required. Several months after I started I remember asking Marscher, "What if we needed more memory?" He assured me that Raytheon could double the memory if needed. He was mistaken. And we would pay a price! The total estimate came to over 42,000 words for each of the CM and LM computers—far more than the 36,864 limit. Kraft assigned his best technical leader/manager, Bill Tindall, to work with us on a joint NASA/MIT requirements scrub program to reduce the size to only those programs essential to the mission. Marscher's Saturn backup guidance program was the first to go since NASA had faith in IBM's ability to program the Saturn flight computer accurately. My Return-to-Earth Program eventually was reduced to a single mode: only the nominal return to a specific splashdown point, eliminating the time-critical and fuel-critical options. However Marscher and I had an idea. I was not the only one who had to solve conic problems. Gerry Levine needed to solve Kepler's Problem for his precision navigation software. George Cherry needed to solve Lambert's Problem for his rendezvous guidance and targeting algorithms. Bob Bairnsfather needed to solve the Time-Radius and Reentry Problems for his Entry Program. They could use my universal, integrated conic solutions as subroutines and save the memory required to solve these problems individually and redundantly. Many other programs had to be scrubbed to fit the memory size.

But now the success of the Apollo mission depended on my conic solutions. Not only did the astronauts have to return to earth safely, but the rendezvous, navigation and entry solutions were fundamental to the mission. This introduced additional requirements for my software package, but only the rendezvous problem gave me pause. I was challenged to meet the 0.5 second time budget for solving Lambert's Problem within every two-second guidance cycle. I got it down to 0.55 seconds, which turned out to be acceptable. After increasing the scope of my responsibility, we turned over the rest of programming the Return-to-Earth algorithm to Tim Brand, who had just joined us after obtaining his MS in Astronautics from Stanford. But the crew voiced another problem. Since my conic solutions had to be scaled to handle every imaginable trajectory to avoid overflow in the fixed-point computers, the resulting granularity of my double precision velocity was 0.25 feet per second (fps). (i.e., the computation of velocity could differ from the previous solution by as much as 0.25 fps.) This caused something called "velocity-to-be-gained bounce" in the crew displays. That is, when rendezvousing the LM with the CM, their closing velocity could be trimmed to only ±0.25 fps because of the inaccuracy in the granularity of the

39

computation. This stayed unresolved during the first few missions and received some notoriety in the inner circles of the NASA/contractor community.

Since now several Lab "customers" used my software, I decided to develop an engineering version of it for simulations on the IBM 650 (we had upgraded from the Honeywell 1800) mainframe. I named the entire package of subroutines for all five conic problems "KWK-CONICS." The package not only solved the problems based on any user's inputs, but printed out a message when someone's data transmitted to any of the subroutines was in error. For example, if someone input a state vector which would take the spacecraft outbound on an escape trajectory, but asked it to solve the Time-Radius or Time-Theta problem which required a return from infinity, my routine aborted the computation with a message that stated "You can't get there from here!" Or if they forgot to input a position and velocity state vector (in effect inputting zeros for the state vector), the routine aborted with "Help! I am at the center of the earth and can't get out." These messages enabled me to avoid repeatedly proving that my programs were not faulty, but rather that my colleagues tried to use the routines with erroneous input data. I'm told that KWK-CONICS is still in use at MIT/IL (now Draper Labs), almost fifty years after I wrote it.

But Dr. Battin was not happy with my solutions to the conic routines. He wanted *his* software algorithms in the Apollo flight computers. I was taking his course in Astronautical Guidance, when he found out I had implemented the Marscher/Krause/Robinson algorithms instead of his own. When I explained that our integrated solution saved so much precious memory (I was able to program all five conic solutions into 1023 words.), he started working to improve his algorithms. Several months later, after I reviewed and rejected several of his attempts to solve the problem, he came up with a more elegant solution than ours. But by this time (mid-1967), it was too late to

40

substitute his solution for ours, which I had programmed, implemented, thoroughly tested, and made available to my "customers." About this time I took his final exam in his famous Astronautical Guidance course. I earned a grade of A in the first semester and had an A going in the second semester. The final exam consisted of three problems. I knew I had solved the first two satisfactorily, but the simplicity of the third puzzled me. Battin never gave easy tests. I poured over the third problem, looking for one of the tricks he had the reputation of laying on us, but could not find it. As I walked out of the exam, I discussed the problem with a colleague only to learn I had misread the problem. What I read as "initial conditions" was really "final conditions," which made the problem much more difficult. When we returned to the office, I told him about my mistake, so he wouldn't think I was a total idiot. His response was, "You have one chance to save yourself, Kurth. Get my algorithms into the flight computers." I didn't, but he gave me a B in the course anyway, instead of the D warranted by the 67 percent grade on the final.

8. *Apollo 1*

But in January 1967 we had a catastrophe. The astronauts selected for the first manned Apollo flight in earth orbit, originally scheduled for February, were Gus Grissom—the second American in space with the Mercury flight; Ed White—the American with the most time space walking outside the Gemini capsule; and rookie Roger Chaffee. I met them during their training on the guidance system at the Lab. They were in the Command Module on top of the Saturn vehicle rehearsing a launch sequence, when a spark—caused by a voltage surge—ignited a fire in the pure oxygen CM environment, killing all three by asphyxiation. They couldn't open the hatch to escape because it was designed to open downward instead of upward and the high pressure caused by the flash fire had sealed it tight. Both NASA and Congress initiated investigations, and the Apollo Program was delayed twenty months to modify the spacecraft design. Joe Shea, a great engineer and NASA's head of the Apollo Spacecraft Program Office, allegedly suffered a nervous breakdown from the tragedy and left the program. The spacecraft contractor, North American Aviation (later North American Rockwell), fired their chief engineer. We at MIT believed

these key people were scapegoats to satisfy the Congress. At the request of their widows, NASA renamed the mission "Apollo 1," in their honor. Grissom and Chafee were buried at Arlington National Cemetery, White at West Point. The Apollo 1 patch was carried to the moon on Apollo 11 and resides there today.

But my days in Massachusetts and MIT were not all work. Our second child was born March 31, 1967. We named her Sheryl Lynn because she was born in Lynn,

Massachusetts. Sue and I were overjoyed that our family was now complete.

The Lab held a party whenever the cash they collected from the Lab's vending machines sufficed. Doc Draper attended each of these and had a table with bottles of alcohol lined up to attract all the young women with free booze. He was quite a personality. He drove a convertible MG with a license plate reading MIT/IL. Even in the cold Cambridge winters, this octogenarian and living-icon drove with the top down, his silk scarf flying in the breeze.

Bill Marscher became a good friend. He took me to Durgin-Park in downtown Boston for their 99¢ lunch; bounced two-year-old Scott on his knees while reciting "Bounce, bounce, bounce to Boston;" taught me to play squash at the Faculty Club; and took me sailing at the Marblehead Yacht Club. I had my first sailing experience with Bill in a nineteen-boat regatta in Marblehead Harbor. He was the captain; I, the crew—and we finished in second place! Others at the Lab were sailors. Three of them owned an eighty-foot International, which they sailed in the Marblehead regattas. When we traveled to Houston to meet with the NASA personnel who needed ideas for their Mission Control ground system software, Bill always scheduled the trips in months with an "R," and we went to the San Jacinto Inn for dinner so Bill could have his oysters on the half shell. However, he was not happy when I stopped playing squash with him during the lunch hour and, instead, played Board-A-Match duplicate bridge with seven others at the Lab.

By August I'd completed my work. Many people were now using my software on the mainframe as well as on the flight computers. After two years at the Lab, I felt reasonably sure I would not be happy going back to GM in Milwaukee since I could not expect anything like my work at MIT.

As my two-year tour at MIT/IL was coming to a close in 1965 and my pending transfer back to Milwaukee, we had a decision to make: should I stay with GM, go to work for MIT/IL, or seek out another company? Once again, the choices were all mine, lulling me into the belief that this would always be the case.

My raises at GM boosted my salary to $1,000/month. The money was important since Sue had stopped working when we started our family. I had leased our home in Milwaukee to three engineering colleagues, which covered the mortgage payments. But I also recognized that if I were willing to change companies, I had an opportunity for more pay. My experience on Apollo at MIT was valuable and in demand. I decided to test the market by interviewing with MIT, IBM Federal Systems in Owego, NY, the defense division of Chrysler in Michigan, and TRW (formerly STL) in Houston.

I dismissed the idea of Chrysler as soon as I learned the work would be boring (fire control system for tanks) in comparison to the exciting and glamorous Apollo Program.

The diverse work at IBM dealt with leading-edge defense industry software development. Also the position would have a perk: free membership in an IBM country club ... very tempting. But the salary offer was low, and Owego's climate unappealing.

MIT/IL offered me a permanent position to join the Lab. The work would continue to be on the cutting technology edge, but they only offered a 10 percent raise. I was also concerned that unless I intended to get my PhD from MIT, I may be at a disadvantage for advancement. They were surprised when I turned down their offer. Marscher seemed very disappointed.

TRW, on the other hand, needed my Apollo work experience. They had won a contract in 1964 to provide technical support to the new NASA Manned Spacecraft Center in Houston which was responsible

44

for the development of the Apollo spacecraft and Apollo Mission Operations. TRW offered me a 25 percent salary increase to move to Houston and join their technical staff. I was also impressed with the office environment, the neighborhoods and the beautiful, new, affordable housing.

In September I accepted the TRW offer, and I gave GM two weeks' notice. We put our Milwaukee house up for sale (one day after the county announced the construction of a new super highway adjacent to our backyard). After the movers packed our belongings, Sue and I packed the kids in our two cars (our 1963 Volkswagen beetle and the 1967 Buick LeSabre that we purchased on the GM employee program), and we were off on the 1600-mile journey for our new adventure. Baby Sheryl was in the crib basket in the back seat of the VW, and two-year-old Scott was in the spacious new Buick. We caravanned, taking turns driving each car.

Although I left MIT/IL in September 1967, and turned down an offer to join their staff permanently, I loved every minute of my two years there. I learned more than I thought possible. I was now one of the world's leading experts in trajectory design and computer implementation. Moreover, my software was used in every Apollo, Skylab, and Apollo/Soyuz mission from 1968-75. MIT awarded me the MIT Certificate of Commendation for my work after the first landing on the moon. In my thirty-six years in the space business, I never experienced such an opportunity again. Original technical work was fun, especially with virtually no management oversight.

A few months after I left the Lab, the student demonstrations against the Vietnam War became demonstrations against the military work being done at MIT/IL. As a result the Lab divested itself from MIT, and became an independent entity named Charles Stark Draper Lab. The Lab now owned the Apollo contract rather than MIT. But my relationships with my colleagues at the Lab were not over.

Regrettably, we only saw Bill Marscher once after that, when he visited us in Texas.

9. *El Lago—A Special Neighborhood*

In the summer of 1967 when I was interviewed by TRW, I had my first view of the bedroom communities that sprang up around the Manned Spaceflight Center thirty miles south of Houston. I was impressed with the homes and neighborhoods in this new environment. Small cities like Clear Lake City, Nassau Bay, Timber Cove, and El Lago had grown up around MSC since its opening in 1963. Although only the first earth-orbit unmanned Apollo missions were just beginning, the engineers, scientists, doctors, and infrastructure in these cities had rapidly developed. The community became a melting pot for the influx of people from all over the country, most directly related to the US manned space program.

Sue and I were twenty-seven years old and we had just started our family. The new schools in this Texas melting pot were excellent and the population highly educated, consisting primarily of young families our age. The weather was better enabling golf year-round—not just the six months dictated by the cold, snowy, gloomy Boston and Milwaukee climates. But I was most impressed by the new homes. We could afford many of the beautiful, large new homes on one-third-acre lots in any of the nearby cities.

We picked out a one-year-old home in El Lago, an incorporated bedroom community of 2,000 residents. For $33,250 we were able to buy this brick home on a corner lot in a cul-de-sac, adjacent to an open lot that was next to a municipal private swim club. The home was magnificent by our standards: 2,400 square feet with four bedrooms, 2½ baths, an enclosed atrium guarding the entrance to a large terrazzo foyer, then on to a great living room, ideal for entertaining. The landscaped yard had all the plants we'd never experienced: yucca, prickly pear cactus, sego palms, and banana trees.

Our house was just four miles from MSC. The Center, built on a campus in Clear Lake City in 1963, had many buildings. It would become the most famous of the NASA facilities, where the astronauts trained, the Mission Operations Control Center controlled all Apollo missions, and the support staff planned each mission.

The El Lago home did not close escrow until two weeks after we arrived. We spent this time in a suite in the Holiday Inn, across from MSC and then gratefully moved into our new home in El Lago. We soon began meeting the neighbors and realized we were surrounded by Apollo astronauts. The Ron Evans family lived two doors away, and the Jerry Carr family—across the street. Bill Anders and his family lived across the cul-de-sac. Next door to Anders was the Charlie Duke family. The Dukes would become our closest friends. Frank Borman and his wife used to jog by our house every morning. Neil Armstrong lived on our same street, Woodland Drive, three blocks down from our cul-de-sac. Dick Truly and his family moved here from California a few years later after the Air Force's Manned Orbiting Laboratory Program was cancelled. Sue became friends with the wife of Story Musgrave. Each of these astronauts became famous when they flew their first missions. Other astronauts also lived in El Lago, but were only passing acquaintances.

The astronauts seemed to settle in clumps in these smaller towns. The vast majority of the first ones, the original Mercury 7 and the next group of Gemini pilots, lived in Timber Cove, on the north end of Mud Lake, the same lake bordering El Lago. The Mud Lake boat ramp was one block from our home. The next several groups, including many of the Apollo and Skylab crews settled in El Lago. The younger groups tended to gravitate toward Nassau Bay, closer to MSC. I knew of only one astronaut in the largest incorporated city in the area, Clear Lake City, where most of the NASA engineers and contractors lived.

Sue and I instantly identified with these families. Most of us had children about the same ages. In El Lago they attended Ed White

Elementary School, named after the astronaut from El Lago who was killed in the Apollo fire in 1967. Many of the mothers helped out in the school, while their yet-to-be-famous husbands gave talks to the students. We all had similar educational backgrounds—typically advanced degrees in aeronautics or astronautics. Of course I did not have the military or pilot experience. We all had recently moved to the community from other parts of the country. Sue and I were a few years younger than most, but we all shared common interests, including the parties, of which there were many.

I did not know Neil Armstrong, personally. Sue had met his friendly wife, Janet, several times, but Neil was a private man. I do remember some of his friends renting a snow-making machine to fill his yard with snow, a rare sight in the warm Houston climate. The kids loved it. In 1971 after his world-famous mission, Neil moved his family to Cincinnati where he was professor of aerospace engineering until he retired in 1979. Scott, as part of his duties as a pilot for President Bush's cabinet, flew Armstrong home from the *Columbia* Memorial Services, which Neil attended with President Bush in February 2003. Armstrong lived in Cincinnati until his death in 2015.

We had fun at the neighborhood parties. The astronauts really knew how to throw a party. Somehow the toddies inspired us to song. I was labeled "the choir director" as I led most of our songs. These were great times we will never forget.

My work on the flight software put me in a special place with my new NASA customers, with whom TRW had our support contract. Ron Berry, the NASA engineer Section Leader at MSC, was my counterpart during my two years at MIT/IL. He was responsible for developing the ground programs for returning the Command and Service Module (CSM) to earth. As a result he asked me to give lectures to his team on the details of my flight software. TRW requested me to do the same for its employees. I wrote specifications on how to duplicate my algorithms for incorporation into TRW's simulation of the CSM, LM, and earth-moon environment. This enabled both TRW and NASA to emulate each mission on their large main-frame computers, and introduce hardware and environmental anomalies to stress-test the software.

10. *To The Moon from Woodland Drive*

After living in El Lago for fifteen months, in December 1968, an exciting event happened. This story is about one of those neighbors: Bill Anders' famous Apollo 8 Mission and his role during Christmas, 1968.

Anders, then a rookie, was selected for the Apollo 8 Mission along with Gemini veterans Frank Borman and Jim Lovell. Apollo 7 was the first Apollo flight with astronauts on board: Wally Schirra, Walter Cunningham, and Don Eisle had proven the space worthiness of the CSM in earth orbit earlier in 1968. Apollo 7 had also demonstrated that my navigation algorithms I had programmed into the CM flight computer worked perfectly. The nearly flawless Apollo 7 Mission, however, was a long way from proving we could get to the moon safely. The delays from diagnosing and fixing the problems exposed by the horrific fire on the pad that took the lives of Gus Grissom, Ed White, and Roger Chaffee had put the Program well behind the schedule set by President Kennedy, to land on the moon and safely return before the end of 1969. The LM was not even completed as yet. We had yet to prove we could:

1. Launch the whole stack with the LM onboard

2. Restart the S-IVB engine for the burn to sufficiently escape the earth's gravitational pull to reach the moon

3. Extract the LM from the S-IVB stage, mating it with the CSM

4. Jettison the S-IVB

5. Navigate to the moon with precision accuracy

6. Ignite the CSM engine to kill off sufficient velocity to be captured in orbit around the moon

7. Separate the LM from the CSM

8. Power up the LM descent engine to first obtain a tighter orbit, then de-orbit and begin the descent to the lunar surface

9. Land safely on the moon

10. Launch the LM ascent stage to get back into lunar orbit

11. Rendezvous in orbit with the CSM

12. Jettison the LM ascent stage

13. Precisely target and restart the CSM engine to return to earth accurately

14. Enter the earth's atmosphere at 24,580 miles per hour at a perfect angle with virtually no margin for error

15. Survive entry without burning up or skipping off into oblivion

It seemed impossible to accomplish all of this in one year. But the NASA decision makers had a plan ... a courageous one.

The next proposed mission was to be a test of the LM in earth orbit. But they decided not to wait for the LM's completion, nor to conduct more manned earth orbit flights with the CSM, since we were not likely to reduce the above listed risks beyond what the successful Apollo 7 had done. Instead, we would attempt to go to the moon with just the CSM! At first they considered just circumnavigating the moon without the major maneuver to go into lunar orbit. But the orbit objective could resolve many more issues. This would test out mission phases 2, 4, 5, 6, 13, 14, and 15 described above. Of course, in the CSM, we could only orbit the moon, not descend, but this was still an extraordinarily bold step with only one manned Apollo mission under our belts. It was decided to try to orbit the moon on Christmas Eve.

Most excitedly for me, my navigation software would be tested on the way to the moon and back, as well as in lunar orbit. In addition, my algorithms that compute how to return to earth from lunar orbit would be exercised in the most critical of circumstances. We were all on edge when the SIVB engine restarted as planned in earth orbit, and then accelerated the spacecraft with its precious cargo of three astronauts to the 24,580 mph velocity necessary for its 240,000 mile journey to the moon. My navigation software was doing its job. My transcendental Kepler's equation, which had worked as expected in the near-circular earth orbit, was now being proven for the near-parabolic translunar trajectory. After two days en route to the moon, they entered the lunar sphere of influence (40,000 miles from the moon), where the spacecraft is more influenced by lunar gravity than earth gravity. At this point my navigation algorithm switched coordinate systems from earth-centered to moon-centered, and the trajectory relative to the moon became a hyperbola. The spacecraft would coast another nine hours before reaching its closest point in back of the moon. The software continued to perform as expected. And as they neared the moon, they prepared for the braking burn that would slow the spacecraft down sufficiently to change the trajectory from a hyperbolic escape to a near-circular orbit around the moon. Since this burn took place on the back side of the moon, we on earth would not know the result until they emerged from behind the moon. The data transmitted to earth matched what we had hoped. They were in lunar orbit on Christmas Eve!

That night the neighbors gathered in the Anders' yard with Bill's wife, Valerie, and their six children. In preparation for the first of our neighbors to go into space with Apollo, we had built a giant American flag, using red, white and blue Christmas lights embedded on a large plywood frame. When Bill was ready for the launch, we erected it in the Anders' yard. We would place this flag in the yard of each of our friends and neighbors whenever one of them went into space. That night we inaugurated this flag. We all sang Christmas carols, and Valerie passed out eggnog. We were out there singing and drinking toddies, when an NBC news crew came with their giant lights to cover our little event. It turned out that this made national TV.

The big story came when each member of the crew read, in turn, their portion of the first verses of Genesis to the world as they saw the earth rise while in lunar orbit. The highlight of the night was the voices transmitted to earth from lunar orbit of the live reading, in turn, verses from Chapter 1 of Genesis by Borman, Lovell, and Anders: "In the beginning, God created the heaven and the earth. The earth was empty, a formless mass cloaked in darkness. And the Spirit of God was hovering over its surface. Then God said, 'Let there be light,' and there was light. And God saw that it was good. Then he separated the light from the darkness. ... And God said, 'Let there be space between the waters to separate water from water.' ... And God said, 'Let the waters beneath the sky be gathered into one place so dry ground may appear.' ... And God called the dry land earth. ... And

God saw that it was good." They closed simultaneously with, "God bless all of you on the good earth."

This was inspired not only by the beautiful blue earth as it rose against the stark, black background of space, (which they witnessed each time their spacecraft came around from behind the moon) but also by their respective Christian upbringings.

But the most anxious part of the mission was yet to come ... the engine restart to get home. Our Return-to-Earth algorithm had to do its job: to calculate the velocity needed to place the spacecraft on an exact lunar hyperbolic trajectory to return them to earth at the precise atmospheric entry angle. Corrections could be made along the way, but only for minor adjustments to the trajectory. Once again, this burn had to be performed on the back side of the moon, and we had to wait to find out if it was successful—and accurate. It seemed like an eternity waiting, but the spacecraft reappeared on time ... a success.

Three days later they splashed down safely in the ocean. Their logo was a great way to depict the "figure-8" free return trajectory in which the CSM flew in front of the moon's path to kill off energy before the burn to put the CSM in orbit. Had the engine been unable to fire this burn, the CSM would have "freely" returned to earth on the second half of this elongated (240,000 by 2200 miles) figure-8 trajectory.

After Bill's return, the Anders invited us over to celebrate with all their friends and neighbors ... the first of many "splashdown" parties. I remember telling Anders the world's biggest understatement, "Bill, I heard you were out of town for the holidays."

He sent us this First Day Cover from the Cape, commemorating the flight.

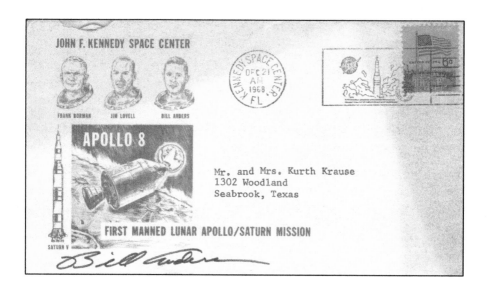

The next year, Bill left El Lago for Washington to take an appointment from President Nixon to the National Aeronautics and Space Council. After serving as Chairman of the Nuclear Regulatory Commission and Ambassador to Norway, he retired from the Air Force in 1977 as a Major General. He moved on to the business world and became CEO and Chairman of General Dynamics in 1991 before retiring in 1993.

Frank Borman retired from NASA as an Air Force Colonel in 1970. He became the CEO of Eastern Airlines in 1975 and Chairman of the Board in 1976. Navy Captain Jim Lovell acclaimed even more fame as commander of Apollo 13. A crater on the back side of the moon is named "Lovell" in his honor. Milwaukee named a museum after him, located on James Lovell Street in downtown Milwaukee. Lovell retired from the Navy in 1973 and was elected President of Fisk Telephone Systems in 1977. In the mid-1990s he served as President of the National Eagle Scout Association. (He had been a Distinguished Eagle Scout while growing up in Milwaukee.)

11. *The Complete Apollo Mission*

To understand the phases of the mission that took us to the moon, I will provide a brief description for each mission phase. It begins with the Vehicle Assembly Building (VAB) 3.5 miles from the launch pad where the spacecraft is mated with the Saturn rocket on a launcher platform mounted on a crawler-transporter. The crawler-transporter was the world's largest self-powered land vehicle in the world, with two tank-like tracked vehicles. It had a maximum speed of one mile per hour to transport the fully loaded Saturn to its launch site 3.5 miles away.

The Saturn V is the tallest (363 feet), heaviest (6.5 million pounds), most powerful (7.6 million pounds of thrust) rocket in the world. It was designed and developed by the team headed by Werner von Braun at the Marshall Space Flight Center in Huntsville, Alabama. The first stage utilizes a cluster of five main engines that burn kerosene and liquid oxygen. The five-engine second stage burns liquid hydrogen and liquid oxygen. The single-engine third stage, the S-IVB, completes the launch by taking the payload into earth orbit as well as later restarting to propel the payload to the moon. The payload consists of the Command Module, the Service Module with its own re-startable engine, and the Lunar Module with its descent engine and ascent engine in a protective housing for launch. On top is a launch escape system to safely power the crew away from the launch vehicle in the event of a launch failure.

NASA engineers designed the coolest, most elegant way to land on the moon and return by discarding each portion of expended hardware all along the way to save weight at each mission phase. The launch window is narrow in time so that the location of the launch pad, moving in space with the earth's rotation, is timed properly with respect to the location of the moon to ensure landing on the side facing the earth for the duration of their stay. After liftoff, the first stage is jettisoned after its fuel is expended at 160 seconds into the boost phase. (Stage 1 burns up as it reenters the atmosphere.) Immediately afterward, the second stage is ignited. Thirty-four seconds later, the launch escape system on top of the CM is jettisoned as it is no longer needed. Stage 2's fuel is expended and the stage jettisoned after eight minutes fifty-six seconds into the flight. (It also burns up as it reenters the atmosphere.)

One second later, eleven minutes twenty-four seconds after liftoff, the S-IVB is ignited and completes the boost phase, shuttling down and achieving earth orbit at a speed of 17,700 miles per hour. After at least one orbit of the earth, NASA Mission Control makes the decision to proceed to the moon. Each of the flight controllers must give a verbal "Go" response to proceed. The S-IVB engine is reignited, burning for 342 seconds to achieve 24,580 miles per hour (just 860 mph less than escape velocity), enough to coast to the moon. Now the CSM separates from the S-IVB and the shroud protecting the LM is jettisoned. The CSM turns around, and docks with the LM, as it extracts it from the S-IVB. Then the spent S-IVB is jettisoned, and actually follows the CSM/LM spacecraft on its coasting trajectory to the moon. As the spacecraft gets farther from earth, it loses speed until 40,000 miles from the moon. At this point the gravity of the moon is stronger than that of the earth, so the velocity of the spacecraft begins to increase until reaching the forward side of the moon. It is on a near-parabolic trajectory as seen by the earth and could freely return to earth after flying by the forward edge of the moon. The lunar gravity "bends" the trajectory around to send it back to earth, resulting in a figure eight. However, ten of the twelve tiny 93-pound reaction control thrusters on the SM will make minor mid-course corrections if necessary to stay on this free return path. This trajectory as seen by the moon is hyperbolic at greater than lunar escape velocity. The CSM/LM coasts approximately 64 hours before it arrives behind the moon. At this point, the SM engine ignites for the

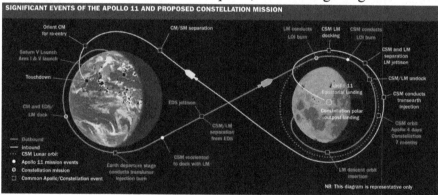

burn to slow the two docked spacecraft into an elliptical lunar orbit, 69 by 197 miles above the lunar surface. At the next pass, the SM engine again ignites to further slow the two spacecraft into a circular orbit 69 miles above the surface. At this point the Commander and LM pilot transfer from the CM to the LM and the two modules separate. Then on the back side of the moon, the LM engine ignites, slowing the LM into a tighter elliptical orbit which coasts down to 50,000 feet on the earth-facing side of the moon. Upon reaching this altitude, the LM engine again ignites to slow the LM speed for landing. The speed is killed off during the burn reducing the altitude until the LM is vertical at 500 feet above the surface. Nominally from this point the LM would descend to the surface at three feet per second. Up until this point, all main descent engine burns are controlled by the computers. But at 500 feet the astronauts take over to tell the LM computer to re-designate the precise landing spot to find the best (smoothest) landing site. The LM has probes attached to each landing pod leg which hang down to sense the instant the LM touches down in order to shut off the engine, inhibiting the descent engine from bottoming out and exploding.

After lunar exploration the crew returns to the LM and prepares for lunar launch. While on the ground, the moon has rotated underneath the CSM orbit. The moon's rotation is naturally synchronized with its orbit around the earth such that the same side always faces the earth. So while the LM was on the surface the moon has rotated a fraction of the lunar month of 27.3 days. The CSM has to burn to align its orbital plane with the launch plane of the LM. The upper stage of the LM performs its ascent burn to rendezvous with the CSM, leaving the descent stage on the moon. The two LM astronauts transfer back into the CM and jettison the LM ascent upper stage, leaving it in lunar orbit. The CSM burn to return to earth is executed on the back side of the moon, escaping lunar gravity and injecting the spacecraft on its near-parabolic earth trajectory home. After any necessary mid-course corrections, the SM is jettisoned and will burn up in the earth's atmosphere. Only the engineless CM returns to a specific splash-down in the ocean. The CM begins to enter the atmosphere approximately 62 miles above the earth at 24,791 miles per hour. It too would burn up if not for the ablative heat shield covering the blunt end of the spacecraft. This shield absorbs the heat and flakes off as it heats up to thousands of degrees, yet keeps the cabin at normal temperature. However, if the angle of entry is too shallow the CM would skip off the atmosphere, like a stone skipping off water, and go back into space. If the angle is too steep, the ablative material would be insufficient to protect the crew and they would perish. Making this dangerous part of the mission even scarier, the heat of entry causes ionization of the air surrounding the spacecraft, blocking out all communication between the crew and Mission Control. The blunt end of the CM acts as a lifting body as it enters the atmosphere, creating a small force pointed away from the velocity vector in order to reduce the G forces. Then the control system invokes a 180 degree roll to dig into the atmosphere to inhibit the CM from skipping out. The crew experiences a maximum force of 7 Gs before slowing down to a near-vertical descent at 100,000 feet above the earth's surface. At 23,000 feet drogue parachutes are deployed. Then at 10,000 feet the three eighty-three-foot diameter main parachutes are deployed, slowing the descent to a safe speed before splashdown.

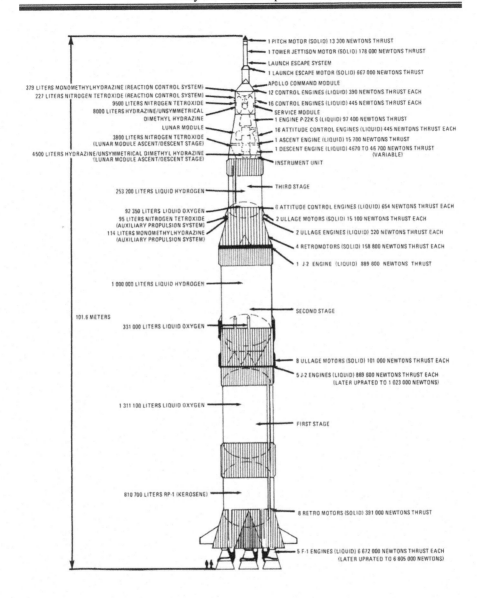

12. *First Management Role*

In March 1969 I was promoted to my first management position, Work Package Manager (WPM). At TRW, a WPM is the first level of supervision in the project office and has total responsibility for the performance of a task under the broader contract—in this case the NASA Apollo Manned Spaceflight Support Contract. Although this was a promotion I had been anticipating, I had no idea how much it would change my career path via management. Up to that point, I had envisioned myself as a technical expert, and based my own measure of job performance on the degree of unique technical contribution I was able to make. Technical performance was still the top measure of success at this level but, as I would soon learn, managing the assets of the team was equally important. I would no longer be responsible for only my personal technical abilities.

The task was to ensure that the Apollo flight software in the LM would successfully perform the two most critical phases of the Apollo Mission: to safely land on the moon and then rendezvous with the CSM back in orbit. My first challenge was to help my NASA customer define the scope of the task. Time was of the essence; Apollo 10 was scheduled for May. The first lunar landing attempt, the Apollo 11 mission, was to follow soon afterward if Apollo 10 were successful. President Kennedy's (and therefore NASA's) goal was to "land an American on the moon and return him safely to earth in this decade." But the NASA Branch Chief responsible for these phases of the mission, Floyd Bennet, was insisting that the scope be limited to only verifying that the flight software as documented in the MIT/IL Guidance System Operations Plan (GSOP) was correct and would work. I disagreed. I argued that if the GSOP was perfect, but the mission failed due to a coding error in the software, then we too have failed. With the help of NASA software expert, Jack Garmin, I succeeded in convincing my customer, Jim Alphin, to broaden the scope. We were given full responsibility to verify that the flight software would perform the two critical phases successfully, a much more challenging task.

This meant the team members would have to understand the flight software code as well as the guidance and control algorithms documented in the GSOP. We would have to read the listings of the assembly language and interpretive language documents to recreate the algorithms, build a scientific simulation of the LM, its guidance system, its environment, and the flight software, and then verify the results for every feasible mission situation. Few at TRW and NASA were qualified to perform this task. Most at MIT/IL were technically qualified, but since they developed the software, their objectivity would be compromised if tasked to verify their own software. Even with my unique experience, there were several idiosyncrasies in the descent guidance algorithms that I had yet to learn.

I was surprised to learn that the selection of my team members would not be up to me. My supervisor, Phil Woodruff told me who he had selected. I was very happy with the choice of Oscar Cerbins, who was one of three TRW employees other than me, who knew how to read the flight software code. Val Azbedian was the only senior team member, mid 30s, former WPM. I had not yet met Val when Phil selected him. I later learned my NASA Task Monitor, Jim Alphin, had been unhappy with Val's previous performance as WPM and had given his work package very low grades. The fourth team member was to be Frank Gerth, a new hire who left his pursuit of a doctorate in theoretical mathematics at Princeton to avoid the Vietnam draft. Working on Apollo would give him a critical skills deferment. I protested this appointment on the basis that Frank could not possibly learn about inertial guidance, navigation, and control, as well as the nuances of flight software in time to make a contribution for the first landing on the moon. I could not have been more wrong.

We had only two months to get ready for the Apollo 10 mission, scheduled for a mid-May launch. The press billed it as a "dress rehearsal" for the lunar landing mission. Although Apollo 10 would not land on the moon, some of the LM software would be exercised. Apollo 9 (March 3-13, 1969) was the first mission to carry the LM, but only in earth orbit. It demonstrated the LM separating from, then rendezvousing and docking with the CSM in earth orbit. But it did not exercise any of our descent or ascent software. The Apollo 10 S-IVB would boost the combined CSM/LM spacecraft from earth orbit to near-escape velocity on a trajectory to the moon. Three senior astronauts: Commander Tom Stafford, CM Pilot John Young, and LM

Pilot Gene Cernan, were selected as crew members, based on their experience from earlier Gemini missions. On the way to the moon (2 ¾ day duration) after the jettisoning the shroud protecting the LM from the atmospheric forces and heat of launch, the CSM would pitch 180° in space, dock with the LM, nose-to nose, and extract it before releasing the S-IVB. Stafford and Cernan were to enter the LM to get it checked out. They would return to the CM for the retrograde burn of the Service Module engine at the back side of the moon to slow the spacecraft down sufficiently for capture in a 69-mile-high by 197-mile-high elliptical orbit. If the LM descent engine did not fire, they would loop around the moon and return to earth 240,000 miles away. If it fired properly, after two orbits, the CSM would perform another short burn behind the moon to circularize the orbit at a 69 mile altitude. Stafford and Cernan would then enter the LM, separate from the CSM, and perform another retrograde burn, this time with the LM descent engine at the back side of the moon, shaping the orbit into an ellipse at 69 miles altitude by 50,000 feet. The final burn on the front side of the moon from 50,000 feet to landing was not to take place for this mission. Instead, they were to jettison the descent stage, and use the LM ascent engine to rendezvous back with the CSM and return to earth. Our ascent guidance and control software would be used for the first time, and my team was to verify it in time for the mission–a tall order in just two months, but at least less of a risk than the landing mission.

Oscar's experience enabled his productivity from the first day. He and I decoded the Draper Lab software programs in a few weeks, working long hours to complete the task. We documented it in a form where the rest of the team could analyze and compare it to that documented by the Draper team in the GSOP. We uncovered several discrepancies, all in the GSOP. Frank was amazing! I piled several books on him describing inertial guidance fundamentals, guidance and control theory, and the GSOP and gave him one week to read and formulate questions for me. I assumed he'd ask rudimentary, superficial questions. Instead, most of them were insightful and demonstrated his quick grasp of the technology and the technical issues. He even asked questions I could not answer. It seemed he had learned in one week what had taken me four years to learn. The guy was brilliant! I couldn't have been happier. NASA also recognized his contribution because after completion of our task the astronauts presented him their Silver Snoopy Award.

I had to travel to Cambridge several times to meet with Alan Klump, author of the LM descent software, to discuss our findings and compare with his. One of these times, I invited Frank to accompany me. On the plane to Boston he read his textbook on Mathematical Topology and, after our meetings, he went on to Princeton and passed his PhD Prelims!

67

I had one other TRW asset I had not really counted upon—John Norton. ...

13. *The Incomparable John Norton*

In my thirty-six-year career I met many intelligent people, some of whom have been described as living legends. But I'm convinced there can be only one John Norton.

Our first encounter was by mail in early 1967. At the MIT/IL we were finally documenting the Apollo flight software for the first lunar landing mission. We had been sending listings of the flight software itself to NASA as we wrote and tested it but, being the pedantic academicians that we were, we tended only to document when we were presenting papers at a technical conference. MSC in Houston had been nagging us to provide this documentation for almost a year. However, they insisted, and we finally acquiesced with the *Lunar Landing Mission GSOP*. We may have released a preliminary version of this 300 page document on Wednesday, but I know I was still making changes to my section on the conic targeting routines final version on Thursday night.

On Friday morning we'd finalized the masterpiece; over three hundred pages of algorithms, equations, and logic were couriered to NASA/MSC by early morning plane. For the expert reader it provided exactly how we were going to target, guide, and control the combined CSM and LM into lunar orbit, separate the LM, descend to the moon and land, ascend back to the CSM, rendezvous, discard the LM ascent stage, and return to earth. Although the documentation had to be sequential, it described how the asynchronous executive operating system would allow any lower-priority program to be interrupted by a higher priority, then would continue to completion when and only when the higher priority program was finished. It described how the guidance cycle had to be completed every two seconds during powered flight and the control cycle, every 40 milliseconds. It was complex. Few people, even at MIT, knew all the details of every program. Although the memory of each of the CSM and LM computers was limited to 36,864 16-bit words, we crammed dozens of programs, a real-time operating system, and an interpreter into each machine. Most of us thoroughly knew only the sections we wrote in the GSOP. Each of us was very proud of our brilliant invention of the algorithms as well as the documentation of our baby. Enter John Norton. ...

On Monday afternoon I came back to my office after lunch. There on my desk was a document at least as thick as the one we sent out on Friday morning. It purported to be "comments" on our Lunar Landing GSOP! "OK, who's the wise guy?" No way someone could have read our document over the weekend, let alone understand it well enough to "comment" on it. It took forty of us over a month to write it. It would take a team of NASA scientists and engineers weeks or maybe months to intelligently comment, and then only after they asked us tons of questions.

I opened the cover. On the first page was a disclaimer: "This document is the sole responsibility of John H. Norton, TRW. Neither TRW nor NASA shall be held accountable for the accuracy of these contents." Now, I **know** it's a joke. I quickly turned to my sections. There were five documented "discrepancies": one typographical error and four "differences" between the actual flight software and what I described in the document—and every comment was 100 percent correct! My astonishment was multiplied by each of the forty MIT authors. Someone explained to me that Norton, a TRW employee in Houston, was contracted by NASA/MSC to review all our flight software products. He well understood how the flight software worked from the code listings we had been sending (Wow!). But even those who knew him by reputation were astonished that he could accomplish this in a weekend!

One year later, when I joined TRW-Houston, I met John and learned how he did it. He is the only person I've ever met who is a technical

70

genius, has a photographic memory, and is a workaholic. He had the CM and LM computer programs memorized perfectly. (I don't know how this is even possible with an asynchronous operating system.) He has no secretary and works alone. He reads the GSOP, page-by-page, and types out what is wrong or inconsistent with his analyzation of the Apollo software working in his head. He could work an entire weekend without much sleep, and loves what he does.

I obviously held him in awe. He knew my software as well as I did, and knew everyone else's perfectly. He chatted about the choices I made, complimented me on the job I had done, but also told me where I could have made improvements. I would go to him with a question about a particular portion of the Apollo software written by others. He would fully answer my question, then dust off a three-inch copy of the listing of the software, turn to the right page, and show me why his answer was correct.

When I managed my first work package to verify the software to take the LM down to the moon ("Descent") and, after landing, back up to the CSM ("Ascent"), I decided to send John a courtesy copy of the first submittal of our findings. I dropped a copy in his office at the end of the day that it was due at NASA. I really didn't think he had the time to read it, but believed he might be interested since he knew so much about the flight software. The next morning at 8:00 AM, I found a "Norton-gram" on my desk. It was a one-page, single-spaced list of errors in our findings. It began with a nice compliment of our discoveries, and then proceeded to list each error. Each of our next two deliverable documents received the same treatment. No matter what time I arrived, John's Norton-gram was on my desk, complimenting our work, and then listing the errors. Finally, I realized I could count on his review. I made it a point to finish a day before the due date, so I could incorporate John's comments and save myself the embarrassment of issuing errata.

John did not always dole out compliments for people's work. In fact his compliments were rare (our work being an exception). I remember a Norton-gram sent to the head of TRW-Houston berating the work of two TRW Departments and their senior managers. One of his conclusions: "If this careless, sloppy work didn't improve, it would someday cost the lives of three Apollo astronauts!" And negative Norton-grams weren't limited to inside TRW. They berated imperfect work of other contractors and even his NASA customer. Norton-grams became a legend in the MSC community, feared by some, read by all. John's direct criticism of anyone who made a mistake set himself up for attack. But he was **never** wrong. MIT/IL once made a comment in the flight software listing that "Norton needs glasses," implying that he misread some of the code. He had not, of course, and he was incensed at MIT's unprofessionalism in a public Apollo document.

What kind of man was John Norton? Most never really knew him. He was a tall, balding man who was socially shy and introverted. He would hug the wall and barely respond to your greeting when you passed in the hall. At large NASA meetings he would never voice an opinion about an issue unless called upon to do so by the NASA manager. But in **his** domain, the quiet of his office where he could call on his knowledge to improve the quality and accuracy of the Apollo quest, he was a terror.

All of Norton's documents contained the disclaimer that neither TRW nor NASA was responsible for the accuracy or content. This stemmed from an episode early in his career. As a young supervisor responsible for the flight software of a missile guidance system, one of his team members made an error. He omitted an overscore in a computer code which caused the computer to recognize the parameter as a scalar rather than a vector. This caused the radar to unsuccessfully search for its lock-on target, causing the guidance system to fail and the range-safety officer to blow the missile up soon after launch. John was devastated and took full responsibility. He submitted his resignation to TRW. Management finally convinced John to stay. But from then on he refused to be in management, preferring to work alone, and used the disclaimer on all his work.

Once, in Houston, TRW management convinced him to work with a brilliant, young protégé on a trial basis, but they did not get along. I think they were too much alike. They always seemed to compete by trying to catch each other in an error.

John was in his mid-thirties when the Apollo missions began. He was divorced, likely due to his incessant work ethic. (He worked seven days per week.) To the best of my knowledge, he had no children. He did become attracted to a young, cute, twenty-something programmer at TRW. In his unique, shy way he left anonymous notes and pieces of candy on her desk at night. I don't believe anything came of this, but many years later I heard he had married again when he transferred to TRW's Virginia facility.

Norton was invariably the person NASA relied on to solve problems, and the only non-executive to receive NASA's highest civilian award: The Distinguished Public Service Medal. John always documented his findings in his Norton-grams … rarely more than one page, single-spaced. But they usually filled the page. And it would take us mortals more than one reading to fully understand it. Some never did.

One day in late 1969 NASA/MSC replaced John's Task Monitor, Jack Garmin, with another well-respected, senior manager, Stan Mann. Under TRW's contract, the NASA Task Monitor would provide a subjective technical performance grade every month, which ultimately determined the fee TRW would earn on its award fee contract. Stan sent out the grades for the first month and awarded Norton a 98 out of a possible 100. John gathered up the thirty documents he had personally generated during the month, stormed over to Stan's office, dropped them on his desk, and challenged,

"Show me where my work is not perfect!" Stan was unable to answer John's challenge. Instead, Stan said he didn't believe in giving grades of 100. The next month, John's old Task Monitor, Jack Garmin, returned along with his perpetual grade of 100.

When the aerospace industry was in a downturn in 1970 and TRW was under pressure by NASA to control their costs, John volunteered to take a salary freeze. Instead, TRW gave him a set of wood furniture for his office, normally granted only to the higher-level managers. When he traveled, he never spent more than $10/day on food, and would report it to the penny on his expense report. But one day he was incensed when TRW denied his claim for a few cents for the postage stamp he used to send some business correspondence.

Years later TRW lost the competition for the NASA Shuttle Support Contract to McDonnell Douglas. Chris Kraft, now Director of the renamed Johnson Space Center (JSC), called the top TRW Space & Defense Executive VP, George Solomon. He offered TRW a sole-source million dollar contract for John Norton to support JSC in evaluating the Shuttle flight software being developed by IBM. Kraft said TRW could staff it with any ten engineers of its choosing so long as one was Norton. Solomon **refused the contract.**

John's new assignment was to return to TRW's West Coast Headquarters to troubleshoot any TRW programs in trouble. He would spend a few days interviewing the program management and key technical personnel, then write up a report listing the technical and management problems and how to fix them. He was more valuable to TRW in this capacity than the million-dollar per year contract offered by JSC. If NASA wanted John that badly, they should have awarded us the $15-million-per-year Shuttle Support Contract. Later, after experiencing the poor performance of McDonnell Douglas, they wished they had.

When I left TRW for Ultrasystems in 1979, TRW threw a going away party for me at a local restaurant in Manhattan Beach, California. Many friends and managers from TRW attended. But I was most astonished and honored by the presence of John Norton, who never attended these things.

John passed away in 2014. He will be sorely missed by everyone at TRW who knew him, but also by NASA and the military. If he were still with us I'd want him to know how much I appreciated his contribution to the US Space Program, his interest in my work, and for being a great mentor to those of us in the field.

14. *Launch of Apollo 11*

To a visitor it seemed like a normal Monday at the JSC community with little evident activity, since the real frenzy was at Cape Kennedy (now called Cape Canaveral). We had long ago completed all our mission planning activities. The final event timeline, trajectory design, testing, simulation, and training had been verified and validated. But everyone was on edge. All of our efforts would become visible to the world beginning in just three days. Did we miss anything? Did one of us slip up on some important detail implemented over the past five years that remained undetected? Could that detail put the lives of three great US pilots, now astronauts, unnecessarily at risk and jeopardize the mission that has excited billions of people on the planet?

This was particularly critical for my team of four engineers. We were charged with the responsibility of validating that the powered descent software was error-free and would navigate, control, and guide the Lunar Module from its lunar orbit down to a safe powered landing. Then, after the moonwalk, the ascent software would execute commands to launch the upper stage of the LM, and guide it back to a safe rendezvous with the CSM.

The ascent and descent programs were not exercised on Apollo 10. So Apollo 11, the First Lunar Landing Mission would, by necessity, be the first real test of our work. What a frightening thought! My team consisted of only one engineer older than I—a "seasoned expert," at 28-years old. The problem with our objective was the impossibility to test for every possible combination and permutation of data which could exercise the myriad numbers of possible paths through the complex software programs. So our job was never truly complete. There was always another different simulation or test case to exercise and maybe find some unexpected or even catastrophic result. Thus my team was more nervous than most, with more than our competence and reputation at stake. At risk were the mission that President Kennedy had promised the world eight years earlier and the lives

of Commander Neil Armstrong (left), Lunar Module Pilot Buzz Aldrin (right), and, possibly, Command Module Pilot Mike Collins (center).

Mid-morning, I received a call from my wife, Sue, which almost made me forget my unending concerns over the LM software. Dotty Duke had called to tell us that her husband, Charlie, had secured two tickets for us to watch the Thursday launch from the astronaut viewing area at the Cape! Charlie was a member of the fifth class of nineteen astronauts to join the manned space program. Although he had never been in space, he was one of three astronauts chosen to be capsule communicators (CAPCOMs) for Apollo 11. The CAPCOMs, in eight-hour shifts, are the only people who directly communicate with the three astronauts during the mission. They relay all information from the flight controller ground crew and, in turn, relay the flight crew's information back to Mission Control. As CAPCOM, Charlie had been at the Cape, rehearsing the mission with the flight crew and obtained the last-minute invitations. Since we were neighbors and close friends, he offered them to us if we could somehow get to Florida in time for the launch. What an opportunity!

The launch was only three days away and the flights and hotels had been booked for months, ever since NASA announced the planned launch date. I immediately called the TRW travel agent to see if she could search for any cancellations. Then I called an old friend at the Cape, Rom Gilbert, who had worked with me at MIT/IL in 1965-67. Rom was currently a contractor supporting NASA's Kennedy Space Center in the role of prelaunch checkout. He was living with his family in Titusville, just a stone's throw from Cocoa Beach and the Cape. Rom and his wife, Lois, were thrilled that we had this opportunity and happy to put us up in their home. They said there was no way we could obtain a hotel room within one hundred miles of the Cape during the days around the launch. They were right. The TRW travel agent came up dry on the hotel room, but eventually, due to a cancellation, got us the last two seats on a National Air Lines flight departing on Wednesday morning for Orlando and returning on Friday. She also got us a rental car. We were in business.

Meanwhile Sue was on the phone to get friends to take care of our two kids, four-year-old Scott and two-year-old Sheryl. Normally the Dukes would take care of Scott and Sheryl, just as we took care of their two boys whenever they went on a short junket. But this time Dotty would also be at the Cape, and, of course, Charlie would be working the mission in Houston. Our other friends and neighbors, the Hubers who knew our kids well, agreed to help out. One last hurdle: I needed permission from TRW for a three-day leave of absence. TRW was wonderful. When I asked my department manager for the time off and told him why, he requested and received the approval from top management to pay for my ticket, travel expenses, and time. Of course, we had to pay for Sue's trip ourselves. TRW also secured an invitation for us to attend a TRW-sponsored liftoff party on a yacht moored in the Banana River. So in forty-eight hours we leaped from wringing our hands in concern over the mission, to a glamorous; exciting; once-in-a-lifetime opportunity to witness the most historical event in the history of the manned space program.

Forty hours later we were flying to Orlando, laden with a car pass to the parkway at the Cape, two guest passes to the astronaut viewing area, and an exhilaration and excitement we could barely contain. We rented a car to drive the fifty miles to Titusville. We checked in with Rom and Lois, whom we hadn't

seen in two years back in Massachusetts. They couldn't have been more gracious and were excited for us. Rom had to be at NASA to support the prelaunch checkout. He had tried to get Lois and their three girls a car pass to see the launch from the road, but he was unsuccessful. They were thrilled when we invited them to come along

and view the launch from our car with the car pass, even though they couldn't come with us to the astronaut area.

We had an exciting night attending parties and receptions, but, were up early the next morning, July 16, 1969. The launch was scheduled for 9:32 AM, but we needed to hit the road by 6:30 to minimize the risk of a massive traffic jam that could prevent us from getting there in time. Although only a few thousand people had car passes to park along the parkway for a good vantage point to see the

Saturn V launch vehicle on the pad, more than a million people were expected to park within twenty miles of the Cape, trying to personally witness this historical event. We arrived more than two hours before the scheduled launch time and parked near the Vehicle Assembly Building. The VAB was, at that time, the largest building in volume on earth. Four Saturn Vs in various stages of assembly could be housed there at one time. It was so big, they had a problem with clouds forming inside and causing it to rain on the workers.

Sue and I left Lois and the girls sitting on top of the car, and made our way to the astronaut area. Along the way, we passed the VIP bleachers, where Lyndon Johnson, Vice President Agnew, and other dignitaries would view the launch, 3.5 miles from the pad. The bleachers were more than half full as we passed. The astronaut viewing area was only three miles from the pad. The only people closer (other than the flight crew) were the NASA launch team members stationed in bunkers to protect them from the fiery launch. When we got to the viewing area, we showed our passes and were issued small American flags. We were all directly in the sun with no chairs or amenities, other than dispensers of lemonade and fresh drinking water. But this made the experience of the event itself more memorable. There were less than one hundred people: astronauts, their family members, and a few others. Dotty was there with her two boys, four-year-old Charles and two-year-old Tom. She introduced us to some of the astronauts we had not yet met, including Alan Shepard, the first American in space, and Charles Lindbergh, the first human to fly the Atlantic Ocean nonstop. History was not only being made, it was being relived.

But the real attraction was three miles away—the Saturn V. My sense of National pride swelled as I became fixated on the gleaming beauty of that white 363-foot high stack and the hot Florida morning sun glinting off the ice forming from the cold liquid propellant in its tanks. At the base was the first stage, a cluster of five S-1 engines, each thirty-three feet wide, each of which would deliver 1.5 million pounds of thrust. On top of it was the S-1B second stage. Upon completion of its burn, it would fall back toward earth and burn up in the atmosphere. Then the third stage, the S IV-B, would ignite to take the spacecraft to earth-orbit. The LM was on top of the SIV-B, hidden from view by a protective shroud. Next came the CSM which housed the three astronauts, strapped down to their couches, facing up to allow the g-forces of the launch to push them back into their seats. On top of the stack was the Launch Escape Tower, which would fire in the event of a launch abort, propelling the spacecraft away from the dangerous lower stage propellant, and deploy a parachute to return them to a safe splashdown. It was an engineering marvel, the culmination of six years of design and development. And now it was ready for the mission promised by President Kennedy just eight years before.

Was it really going to happen? The NASA voice from the mounted speakers begins the countdown—"Thirty minutes to launch." We have no assurance that the launch will take place today. Only one of the four previous Apollo launches had taken off as scheduled. So many things can go wrong: weather visibility problems at the Cape, the emergency recovery locations, or the early tracking stations; high winds; anomalies in any of the thousands of vehicle checkout parameters; crew illness; and also equipment problems at Kennedy, MSC, or the tracking sites. Today's weather is near perfect; the clouds seemed to part just in time for the launch.—"Fifteen minutes to launch."—The launch window is only two hours long.[2]—"Five minutes to launch."—My hands are perspiring. It is both exciting and frightening. I wonder what the crew is feeling right now. I can't help but think of the worst-case disaster—the catastrophe of the vehicle blowing up on the pad, as happened so many times in America's earlier days of developing launch vehicles in the late '50s and early '60s. But the final countdown proceeds as the gantry support falls away.—"10...9...8... Engine Ignition!" —We see the flames start to spew out from the five S-1 engines—"7...6...5...4...3...2..." —Three giant rocker arms hold the six-million ton stack in place while the engines build to 90 percent of their 7.6 million pounds of thrust.—"We have liftoff!"—Right on schedule!

---

[2] The launch window is the time span during which the launch point on the spinning earth, and the moon in its orbit around the earth, are properly aligned so that only a nominal plane change is necessary for the orbital plane of the spacecraft to be in the proper orientation for the translunar trajectory. If any problem caused a long enough delay to miss the launch window, the launch would have to be postponed. If the delay were more than three days, the next launch window wouldn't open until the next lunar month.

Sue's Painting of the Apollo 11 Launch

At first we hear nothing, but see the rocker arms unleash their hold, allowing the initial acceleration of only 1.15 times gravity to slowly lift the beautiful stack off the pad and up the gantry. It seems to move so slowly at first, almost surrealistically so we can savor the moment. (The engines are consuming fuel at 4,500 gallons per second.) Still no sound since we are three miles away and sound travels at $\frac{1}{5}$ mile per second. The majesty of the vision grabs me, putting a lump in my throat. As the Saturn V proceeds halfway up the gantry, we begin to hear the "pop, pop, pop" of the S-1 engines, now getting louder and more frequent, until it engulfs us in a wall of sound. We almost want to run as the sound envelops us in a blanket of deafening thunder. But I get used to it as the beautiful sight of this magnificent machine, climbing straight and true, begins its roll maneuver to the desired azimuth for the pitch into the planned launch plane. My eyes well up with tears as the cheering and flag waving begins. I am feeling an immense pride. And I realize that this pride is not caused by my personal work on the flight software but, rather, in the pride I have of being an American. And it is so much richer.

As the fuel rapidly depletes, the Saturn V gets lighter, and the acceleration proportionally increases to 4½ Gs. The Saturn and its five flaming engines quickly disappear into the sky. We think we see separation of the first stage as the second stage ignites but are unsure. It does not dampen the cheering and celebrating, as we are now sure the launch is successful. The relief is overpowering. Pandemonium is erupting. It is time to party with these wonderful, cheering, frenzied people who have shared in the witnessing of the first successful step of the journey to land Americans on a different celestial body in our solar system.

15. *The First Lunar Landing*

I was still in a euphoric state as we arrived in Houston, back from the Cape. What a launch! What a high! But the best was yet to come. (Could it really be more exciting than yesterday's launch that we got to see firsthand?)

It was the afternoon of July 17, 1969. Neil Armstrong, Buzz Aldrin, and Mike Collins had jettisoned the S-IVB stage after it propelled them on the near-parabolic trajectory to the moon. Neil and Buzz had entered the LM through the docking tunnel from the Command Module, powered up and checked out the equipment. Almost three days to wait as they coasted weightlessly toward the moon. The names the astronauts chose for their spacecraft were *Columbia* for the CM and *Eagle* for the LM.

Back at work, my verification team busily ran simulations, looking for any possible bugs that might cause problems in the descent to or ascent from the lunar surface. But it was hard to keep our minds on the work, with one eye and one ear following the fortunes of the mission. Of course, this was the most uneventful phase—coasting to the moon with only minor mid-course corrections to tune the trajectory to its precise point where the SM engine must start its braking burn to achieve lunar orbit. (No one dreamed of the danger in **this phase** of the mission, but the world would become totally aware of the dangers just two missions later.)

As head of the team responsible for verifying the ascent and decent guidance, navigation, and control software, I was honored to be invited to the backup Mission Operations Control Room (MOCR) at MSC in Clear Lake City for the landing. It was July 20, just one day before my 29th birthday. I left my TRW office right after lunch and walked the half mile to MSC. The afternoon of July 20 was a typically hot (90+ degrees) and humid (90+ percent) Texas Gulf Coast day. I arrived in the backup MOCR with a lump in my throat, sat down at the guidance console in the front row, and excitedly started to call up the displays.

The flight team controls the mission in the primary MOCR in real time. Once the launch vehicle clears the tower, the MOCR team (i.e. "Houston") takes over. For security reasons the building has no windows. A dozen flight controllers and their assistants man the main floor. Each has his own console to call up his specialty displays. Some of the key players: the Flight Director (FLIGHT)—in complete charge of every decision by the ground crew for the mission, including the Flight Dynamics Officer (FIDO), the Guidance Officer (GUIDO), the Retro Fire Officer (RETRO), and the Capsule Communicator (CAPCOM). Three shifts control the mission twenty-four hours per day. The top crew, of course, manned the most important phase of powered landing on the moon. The crew: FLIGHT, Gene Kranz; the GUIDO, twenty-seven-year-old Steve Bales in charge of the Primary Guidance, Navigation, and Control System decisions; and the CAPCOM, astronaut Charlie Duke—our neighbor and friend who had arranged for us to see the launch in the Astronaut Viewing Area at the Cape.

In the back of the MOCR, the VIP area is where approximately thirty people—usually the families of the flight crew and dignitaries—sit in theater-type chairs, sealed off through a wall of glass to watch the action on the main floor. For this phase of this all-important mission, the families were not invited into the MOCR, but were at home listening to all the crew and controller conversations fed through a direct line on a "squawk box." Politicians, space pioneers—including Dr. Charles Stark Draper of MIT and top NASA management—including Administrator Thomas Paine, Marshall Space Flight Center Director Werner Von Braun, and MSC Director, Robert Gilruth—jammed the VIP room.

The backup MOCR is one floor below and identical in every way to the primary, so that in an instant, should anything go wrong, the flight controllers can move downstairs and use it as primary. That day the key technical people who were responsible for the program filled our floor. Dr. Richard Battin, my former boss at MIT/IL responsible for all the flight software, sat at the console directly behind me. George

Cherry, Battin's lead for the LM programs, was at the console next to him. The VIP area overflowed with other dignitaries, just as in the primary MOCR upstairs.

As I sat down at the console, the *Eagle* crew had just received the latest update to their state vector from the CAPCOM and prepared to start the Descent Orbit Insertion (DOI) burn. The *Eagle* had earlier separated from Mike Collins in *Columbia*. This burn of less than one minute would reduce *Eagle's* velocity only enough to cause the circular orbit, sixty-nine miles above the lunar surface, to change to an ellipse, with the closest point to the surface at 50,000 feet altitude. The burn was scheduled to take place on the opposite side of the moon from the earth, so their lowest point—pericynthian—would be on the front of the moon in full view from the earth, at which point they would start their landing maneuver. To accomplish DOI on the backside of the moon, they would lose communication with the earth. This made the burn more exciting and nerve wracking for all of us on the ground. Both *Columbia* and *Eagle* would lose earth contact as they disappeared behind the moon. *Eagle* would perform its burn with only Collins observing it, and we on the ground would not know whether it was successful until the *Eagle* reappeared, hopefully at the exact time expected, based on the planned burn duration. To be precise, both telemetry and voice signals travel at the speed of light. So it takes 1.3 seconds to reach the earth and (2.6 seconds round trip.) The gigantic three-panel display at the front of the MOCR could show only the simulated orbit, assuming the burn was executed as planned. My console could not help either, since its information on the actual state vector was an extrapolation of where the LM had been as it encountered Loss of Signal in going behind the moon. The tension was immense. It seemed no one dared to breathe.

A cheer went up, followed by a collective sigh of relief, as *Columbia* and then *Eagle* came out from behind the moon on time and acquired signal. Information from the crew, through the CAPCOM, indicated the burn had executed perfectly. Finally they were ready for the most dangerous part of the mission: the lunar landing.

Eagle was still whipping past the lunar surface at 4,000 miles per hour at 50,000 feet. The LM descent engine must ignite again to start to kill off this velocity with a braking maneuver, and *Eagle* would begin its descent to the lunar surface. Armstrong and Aldrin could not see the surface at first. They were flying with their window up and away from the surface, so the engine could fire opposite to their forward velocity. Only after the burn had nullified much of the velocity would the LM pitch up after "Highgate," such that they could begin to see their intended landing site, while the engine was pointed more downward to kill off the vertical speed. Later in the burn at "Lowgate," their orientation was almost vertical as the throttle-able engine would bring them to a slow descent. At this point the astronauts took over manual control to bring *Eagle* to a soft, safe landing. They would try to maintain descent at three feet per second (fps) as they selected the best available flat and smooth lunar surface for touchdown. They could re-designate the landing site with two-dimensional correction commands to the computer's autopilot, which would in turn control the pitch and yaw of the engine gimbals. The landing itself was critical, not just because of the danger of a crash. If *Eagle* came in too fast and the bell of the engine buried in the lunar dust before the engine was turned off, it could explode. If they landed on a slope or a boulder, *Eagle* could tip over prohibiting vertical ignition of the ascent stage to return to rendezvous with *Columbia*. If they descended too slowly, they could run out of fuel and would have to abort, jettisoning the empty descent stage and igniting the ascent engine.

While thinking about all this, Armstrong, Aldrin, the ground crew, and the spectators waited for the flight controllers to make their Go/No-Go decision to begin the final burn. Gene Kranz verbally polled his team of flight controllers: FIDO ... "Go!" ... GUIDO ... "Go!" ... RETRO ... "Go!" ... CAPCOM ... "Go!" until all unanimously confirmed their decision to begin the burn. Each "Go!" acknowledged viewing nominal parameters within an acceptable margin of error on their respective specialized console screens. My hands began to perspire. The descent engine ignited.

My console showed the powered trajectory to be A-OK. The velocity was slowing just as we had simulated hundreds of times. Suddenly Aldrin announced a surprise that made my blood run cold. I could see it on my screen: 1202 Alarm! This meant the program queue in LM computer was full. At least one program requested execution, but the full computer's program list kept locking it out! Eight programs were running, sharing computer resources ... no room for any more. "Impossible," I thought. We had never seen this in any of our simulations. What program was not being executed? Aldrin said it again, "1202 Alarm!"... And again! ... And again! Then he announced, "1201 Alarm!" This meant one or more programs, which were in the queue, were not getting completed within the allotted two-second guidance cycle time. What was wrong with the computer? What was wrong with the software? **What did we miss in our testing?** We'd painstakingly worked out every detail of the time allotted for each needed program and executed it in a simulated environment hundreds of times. This can't be happening!

As they approached Highgate, Kranz polled his flight controllers for a Go/No-Go decision. If any recommended "No-Go" and Kranz agreed, he would order Armstrong to hit the Abort Button, which would shut down the descent engine, and ignite the ascent engine to carry the crew in the upper part of the LM on a trajectory to rendezvous with Collins in *Columbia*. Armstrong did not need Kranz's directive to abort. If he thought *Eagle* was in danger, he had the authority to abort at any time without ground input.

When Kranz got to GUIDO, Steve Bales yelled "**GO!**" in a high-shrilled falsetto-like voice. Obviously he too felt as panicked over this set of unexpected circumstances as I. And he was responsible for the real-time guidance decision. But, despite the alarms, the trajectory looked good. The NASA Task Monitor, Jack Garmin, in the Staff Support Room next door also saw this and advised Bales to continue. Steve made his decision. Had it been up to me, I would have aborted.

Now, *Eagle* having pitched up, the crew could see where they were heading—into a boulder field! We had purposely targeted the landing site to a flat area in the Tranquility basin to preclude the problem of trying to avoid landing on a boulder or the bank of a crater. What happened? The display in the cockpit had now changed to show range to the site (distance to land), range rate (speed of descent), and a geographical indication of the designated landing point. Armstrong re-designated the landing point to avoid the boulders.

But the Alarms kept coming, interrupting the important display information nearly half the time: "1201!" ... "1202!" ... This had to be hampering Armstrong's ability to home in on the best site. Lowgate was approaching. Kranz polled again: FIDO ... "Go!" ... GUIDO ... "**Go!**" The trajectory still looked good. Where do they get their cool? I had a better appreciation as to why a prerequisite for these pilot astronauts was success as a test pilot. But were they too cool? Maybe foolhardy? Why not abort, return safely, give us time to figure out the problem, fix it, and try again in a few months? We could still meet Kennedy's goal to land in this decade. If they crashed, the program could die with them.

As planned, at 500 feet above the lunar surface Armstrong took control. Aldrin dutifully barked off the display readings of range (now altitude), range rate (now altitude rate), and landing site designation. Armstrong had to continue to tweak the landing site to find a safe, flat surface and to bring the *Eagle* down at nominally three feet per second, using the display information from Aldrin while intently peering out the window. But the alarms continued, interrupting the nominal display every few seconds. Armstrong had burned up a good portion of the fuel reserve in avoiding the boulder field and now had to get on the ground quickly or abort. "Down" ... "400 feet, -4 fps" ... "re-designation" ... "200 feet, -2 fps" ... "150 feet, +1fps" ... "thirty seconds of fuel left," ... "50 feet, -2 fps" ... "shadow" ... "contact" ... "engine off" ... "touchdown!" ... "The *Eagle* has landed!" CAPCOM

Charlie Duke said, "You got a bunch of guys here about to turn blue. We're breathing again. Thanks a lot."

The cheering went on and on. It didn't seem to stop. Five hundred million people watched TV live. I got up from my console and walked back to congratulate Battin and Cherry. Both seemed stunned. Battin had paled. Neither said much. Armstrong had landed with eighteen seconds of fuel left. But what caused the computer alarms? And why did they land in a boulder field?

Of course TRW's John Norton and NASA's Jack Garmin figured it out. Aldrin followed the recently modified flight control rules to turn on the Rendezvous Radar Switch during descent just in case of an abort ... one less switch they wouldn't have to worry about in the frenzy of an abort. So the programs trying to get on line, but locked out, were the targeting routines to rendezvous with *Columbia*. When they did get in the queue, they weren't being completed. Fortunately they were designated a lower priority relative to the critical powered descent programs. Why didn't we or MIT/IL or NASA and the flight crew at two Apollo trainer/simulators at MSC and the Cape ever see the problem? The switch was never connected in the simulator for this phase of the mission. Only a few NASA people even knew they had made this change in the flight rules—to turn the switch on prior to starting Descent. The fix for all future missions, of course, was to keep the switch off until an actual abort decision was made.

We on the inside considered Steve Bales and my NASA customer, Jack Garmin heroes (along with Armstrong and Aldrin). Bales had the responsibility to make the decision and did it by the book. A twenty-seven-year-old flight controller had saved the mission by staying cool enough to rely on his training and discipline, not panic (as I would have), and with Garmin's help, make the right decision.

Everyone celebrated that afternoon and evening. TRW, like so many other Apollo contractors, sponsored a great party around the

swimming pool at the Holiday Inn on NASA Road 1. We'd done it! We had landed a man on the moon in this decade. But we still had to get them back safely. Would the Eagle's ascent engine fire off the descent stage properly? Would the small ascent stage properly rendezvous with *Columbia*? Did I miss something else in verifying the ascent software?

Risks still loomed. Still, this event was the shot in the arm America needed in a decade of chaotic, tragic events that had caused our country to question its leadership position in the world. The '60s had given us the cold war, the Cuban missile crisis, riots in our cities, violence on our campuses, rampant drug abuse, the sexual revolution, the Kennedy and King assassinations, the Bay of Pigs fiasco, the

Vietnam War, and disrespect for our military. Landing astronauts on the moon restored a sense of American pride, where it had been eroding throughout the '60s. And I had been a part of it. Whatever else happened in my next thirty years in space could never top this. I received awards from NASA, MIT, and TRW for my roles in this achievement.

Left to right: TRW GM and Operations Manager Ed Goldberg, Kurth Krause, TRW VP Bill Besserer

16. *Apollo 12—The Luster Begins to Fade*

After celebrating the unbelievable success of Apollo 11, we expected a letdown. We had done it! We had landed two Americans on the moon in this decade and brought the three-man crew back safely to earth, as President Kennedy had challenged the space program to do in his inauguration speech in 1961. And we had done it with five months to spare. Inevitably the luster for the rest of the nine Apollo missions planned for exploration of the moon would not reach the same magnitude. But the depth and breadth of the news media tail-off surprised me as we readied for the launch of Apollo 12.

Our success energized us. The fact that we had found the anomaly in the crew procedure that caused the computer overload alarms during the powered descent to the lunar surface also drove us. Officially, my responsibility was limited to ensuring that the software would perform successfully. And indeed it had. Crew procedures were the responsibility of the NASA flight controllers and the astronaut crew. Even if we had flagged the extremely tight computer time margins in nominal program execution, the NASA team likely would not have recognized the impact of changing the crew procedures to set the rendezvous radar switch to "ON," as a cautionary measure during descent. The simple fix for Apollo 12 was: keep the switch "OFF" as originally planned, inhibiting the rendezvous programs from being invoked during lunar descent.

My independent verification team used the four months between flights to full advantage. We updated our simulation, changed our version of the guidance and control software to match the minor changes introduced by MIT into the flight software, and continued our detailed analysis of the results. We found and reported on minor flaws in the powered descent and ascent guidance software—the most significant, a potential for the descent guidance algorithm to cause a "ringing" oscillation of the LM descent engine in the final seconds of landing. But this was not critical since the mission rules called for the crew to override the guidance commands during the final 500 feet to touchdown. Everything was ready for the November 14th launch.

The launch went flawlessly. Yet the news media, which had lauded Apollo 11 as the greatest accomplishment of the decade, had now started to turn against the program. I remember my favorite anchor, Walter Cronkite, negatively quoting the cost of the fuel being burned by the Saturn rocket instead of describing this beautiful launch vehicle rising majestically from the tower. I was shocked at how quickly and callously the media could turn. But then, I was still a naïve twenty-nine-year-old and obviously biased by my involvement.

As a reward for the work my team had done (and in case I could add some technical assistance), my NASA Task Monitor, Jim Alphin, invited me to join him and Jack Garmin in the Staff Support Room at Mission Control in Houston during Lunar Descent. These NASA personnel provided the detailed technical knowledge required by the Flight Controllers to handle any anomaly or contingency encountered during the mission. This time we encountered none.

Apollo 11 overshot the intended landing site by three miles, due to our lack of an accurate gravity model of the mass concentrations in the lunar surface. These mascons are now believed to be caused by dense asteroids and comets colliding with a molten moon billions of years ago. NASA had used the tracking of *Columbia*'s lunar orbit to upgrade the science community's gravity model, which we incorporated into both the Apollo onboard and Mission Control Center navigation software. This time we hoped to be much more accurate in finding the landing site, near the spot where NASA had landed an earlier, unmanned lunar probe, the Surveyor. But we would not know until the LM astronauts, Commander Pete Conrad and LM pilot Alan Bean, could actually see the lunar terrain from the LM window. Since the astronauts face upward, away from the lunar surface, during most of powered descent, they cannot see the surface until after "Highgate" (the point at which the LM is rapidly pitched upward and the window is pointed downrange). Conrad, probably the most excitable and animated man in the astronaut corps, went absolutely bonkers soon after Highgate occurred because he could see the Surveyor. He started screaming "There it is! Son of a gun! We're right down the middle of the road! I can't believe it! Fantastic!" His enthusiasm electrified all of us. We shared his thrill. They landed 538 feet from the target in the Sea of Storms. Once again, after a near perfect mission and splashdown, we partied.

Twenty-seven years later, just a few months before Pete died in a motorcycle accident, he gave a speech at my country club's monthly men's program. He was the same enthusiastic guy, then CEO of a company that planned to build a new low-cost space launch vehicle. After his talk, he and I reminisced about his  thrilling ride to the moon, as if it happened just yesterday. Too bad the rest of the public couldn't share this thrill. I played golf a few months later with Dick Gordon, Pete's Command Module pilot on Apollo 12. He too was a guest speaker at our men's program. I enjoyed introducing him to my golf partners.

The Apollo program was rapidly cut back in funding, and the planned number of lunar missions reduced by three. Many astronauts would never experience this thrill. Moon rocks and exploration were deemed less important than funding for the Vietnam War and the legacy of

Lyndon Johnson's social programs. The layoffs were extensive, primarily in Houston, Florida, and California. TRW, as all the Apollo contractors in the area, had to cut back.

My team was safe since we had more work to do for the upcoming missions. However I experienced my first dose of reality—the first of many times that I saw a downturn, usually followed by a buildup five to ten years later.

We were not hit as hard as some. Rockwell, Grumman, McDonnell Douglas, and their hardware subcontractors suffered the most, since no Saturns, CSMs, and LMs were needed for the cancelled Apollo 18, 19, and 20 missions. The laid off engineers had difficulty finding new jobs. No new programs required their unique skills. Employers actually had ads that said, "Aerospace need not apply." What a blow! PhDs found themselves driving taxis for a living ... from the darlings of the world to unemployed and shunned in a few months. And the colleges and universities made it worse.

Somehow academia is often five years behind the power curve. When the industry is at its peak, they advise new freshmen to major in the sciences. Later, at graduation they face the downturn because their skills are in abundant supply. Yet, when these skills are needed most, due to a buildup, few are graduating because the "advisors" told the incoming freshmen five years earlier that the aerospace industry had no jobs available.

Our government, of course, was the primary cause of the problem. We did not have a smooth multi-year plan for the aerospace needs and the corresponding funding. Each program was funded annually with major changes and cancellations, particularly when a new party was in power. This resulted not only in the "feast and famine" buildups and layoffs, but also in major wastes of resources—both people and money—particularly when programs and plans were cancelled.

17. *The Most Successful Failure*

After the highly successful Apollo 12 flight touched down on the moon without a problem, precisely on the planned landing site, and then safely returned, the country and the Apollo team seemed to relax. Why not? We proved we could do what had never been done before, and did it with elegance and precision—twice! We were great. We were invincible. We were masters of the universe. We could—and would—do it again and again. The liftoff and splashdown parties escalated.

We readied for the next flight: Apollo 13, with the popular crew of Commander Jim Lovell, CM Pilot Ken Mattingly, and LM Pilot Fred Haise training to land on the interesting Fra Mauro region of the moon. The launch was scheduled for April 11, 1970. I had recently been promoted to Section Head, a first-level supervisor at TRW, supporting the Apollo mission planning for the Johnson Space Center. One part of my team helped to map out each phase of the mission in earth orbit, the trans-lunar trajectory, lunar orbit, and the trans-earth leg prior to reentry into the earth's atmosphere. Another part of my team once again performed the independent verification and validation of the integrity of the flight software for the LM's powered descent to the moon and the ascent back to the CM. All went smoothly prior to liftoff.

But not all was routine for the astronaut crew. Our friend Charlie Duke had come down with German measles one week before the flight. Unfortunately, the primary crew had been exposed to Charlie prior to this time, because Charlie was the backup LM pilot. Four days before the flight the NASA Administrator, Tom Paine, made the decision to replace Mattingly (the only crew member who might be susceptible to measles) with backup CM pilot Jack Swigert. It was important to ensure that no one would come down with the measles during the eight-day mission in such close quarters as the LM and

CM. This was not an easy decision. The backup crew was there to fully replace the primary crew as a contingency. Each crew trained together for almost two years. But NASA could not replace the entire crew since Charlie was a member, forcing intensive training of Swigert with Lovell and Haise for the few days prior to liftoff. Mattingly was devastated.

However, the liftoff went well with only minor glitches during the first two days of flight. The docked LM, CM and Service Module, which housed the Apollo spacecraft's main engine and fuel, were well on their way to the moon on the planned trajectory. Joe Kerwin, the astronaut CAPCOM, even remarked, "The spacecraft is in real good shape as far as we are concerned. We're bored to tears down here." **Ironic**. Almost fifty-six hours into the mission, the crew finished a TV broadcast, and Lovell said "good night" to the viewers. Ten minutes later, 193,000 miles from earth, it happened: One of the two liquid oxygen tanks blew up, damaging the other, lighting up alarms like a Christmas tree on the CM control panel, causing Swigert to make his famous announcement, "Houston, we've had a problem." Two of the three fuel cells fed by the oxygen were lost, causing a near catastrophic degradation of the electrical power supply. Initially no one fully appreciated the gravity of the damage. It would become a

struggle to survive!

Back on the ground, my team, along with hundreds of others, was called to action. The mission, of course, had to be aborted. We had to help the Flight Controllers decide whether to try to get the crew back directly by turning around and firing the SM engine for a major burn, or to allow them to circumnavigate the moon, making only small burns to adjust the trajectory for a "normal" reentry. These choices were well known to me. While I was at MIT, before we ran out of memory in the flight computers, my Return-to-Earth Program had two other options besides targeting to return to a precise splashdown point. If time were critical, my targeting program would burn all the fuel to get back as soon as possible. If fuel were critical, it would calculate the optimal point on the current trajectory to get back by burning the minimum amount of fuel. Now these options were no longer in the onboard computers, but in only the ground computers.

But in Apollo 13, though initially no one had sufficient knowledge of the extent of the problems, we would find that both the fuel and the time were critical. We did not know whether the SM main engine would even fire. And we did not know the extent of the time problem in using up the electrical power to service the CM systems, such as the main engine, inertial guidance, and the life support systems, including the cabin temperature. Although the astronauts were more than eighty-seven hours from home, the Flight Controllers decided to continue on the circumlunar trajectory. While the nominal trajectory needed only minor navigational corrections to return to earth, the Apollo 13 path had been modified to reach the Fra Mauro lunar landing site, and therefore had to be put back on the proper "free return" trajectory. The ground crew decided to use the LM's descent engine (built by TRW under subcontract to Grumman) for this burn, in order to save precious CM power. The crew transferred to the LM, using it and its human support systems as a lifeboat. They fired its attitude-control jets to adjust the trajectory for midcourse corrections.

However, the LM was not designed to support three astronauts for the nearly four days it would take to get back to earth. And even if it did, we still had another major concern: we had no way to know whether the heat shield, so critical for surviving the enormous heat of reentry, was damaged. But the ground crew had to develop the procedures for using the LM in this way, on the fly. Neither they, nor the crew, with all their contingency training, had envisioned the needs created by the explosion.

As the full extent of the damage was revealed, I almost lost hope of getting them back alive. This was the first mission that, as a manager, I was only indirectly involved technically and was not sequestered with my team in Building 30 at the Center. Therefore, my information was less as an insider and more as an observer. Unlike my sequestered team, I had plenty of time to reflect on the unfolding ominous drama. I was frightened and becoming depressed as I learned more about the problems.

The ground crew, which included Ken Mattingly, Charlie Duke, and John Young, developed many of the makeshift procedures that got the flight crew through their unbelievable ordeal, and were the real heroes of Apollo 13. Many of the ground crew, my team included, worked almost continuously throughout the more than three days it took to get them back, only taking occasional catnaps to try to clear their minds. No one went home. Gene Kranz, the most senior and, arguably, the best of the three shifts of Flight Directors—including Glynn Lunney and Gerry Griffin—was quoted on his direction to his ground crew, "Failure is not an option." This became the title of his outstanding book on Apollo 13, in which the reader can almost relive those hours through the eyes and emotions of the ground team.

The 1995 docudrama "Apollo 13," directed by Ron Howard, well portrayed the miraculous story. Tom Hanks played the role of Jim Lovell. It held to the facts almost perfectly. Hanks has always been a space buff and intensely interested in the Apollo program. I prepared myself to be disappointed with the accuracy of the re-creation when Sue and I saw the film for the first time; instead I was impressed. Only minor details (e.g., the timing of the decision to replace Mattingly and the number of hours it took to locate Mattingly after the explosion) were incorrect. Howard could have emphasized the heroic acts of the ground crew more and de-emphasized the role of the flight crew, who had no choice but to implement everything invented by and directed from the ground. But his emphasis on the astronauts was expected, and more acceptable to the doting general public. In 1998, Hanks did another excellent job with his twelve-part series on Apollo for the HBO television network, "From the Earth to the Moon."

As history recorded, of course, the many new procedures and fixes worked, and after some harrowing and life-threatening periods during the return to earth, the crew returned safely. And we had the biggest splashdown party of all.

A few days after the crew was safely home, Grumman, who built the LM, sent a bill to Rockwell—builder of the CM and SM—for "towing services." Grumman plastered a replica of it on billboards throughout our community. We all enjoyed the joke.

Jim Lovell was one of the most personable and likeable astronauts. I never really knew him well. But I talked with him at length at the Twentieth Anniversary of the First Lunar Landing. I was impressed with his candor and absence of ego. He had attended my alma mater, the University of Wisconsin, prior to entering the Naval Academy at Annapolis. He was selected as an astronaut when I graduated in 1962. He and Frank Borman were the first to ever rendezvous in space on Gemini 7; he was one of the first humans to orbit the moon on Apollo 8; and he held the record for most hours in space (715) up until the Skylab Program. Lovell retired from the astronaut corps and the Navy in 1973. Subsequently he worked as a businessman at several small companies, holding offices such as President, CEO, Director and Chairman of the Board. Earlier he had served as President Nixon's Chairman of the Physical Fitness Council, an office he held for eleven years.

Apollo 13 was Fred Haise's first and only mission. He retired from the astronaut corps and became a Vice President at Grumman, the manufacturer of the LM. He later headed the Grumman team at Cape Canaveral, which had a major role in refurbishing and readying the Shuttle for each launch. Later, he was the Program Manager and President of a Grumman subsidiary responsible for helping NASA manage the development of the International Space Station (ISS). As General Manager of Intermetrics, I briefed him several times on how we could help him manage the flight and ground software elements of the program, but he never got around to putting us on the team. One year later, when it became clear the ISS Program was mismanaged, Grumman lost this billion-dollar contract for inadequate performance.

Jack Swigert also retired from the astronaut corps in 1973, becoming the US House of Representatives Executive Director for US Space and Technology. He was elected to the House from Colorado in 1982, but died of cancer before taking office.

Ken Mattingly must have had divine guidance. Although Mattingly never came down with measles, Ken's role in developing the fixes and procedures to enable the crew to cope with their oxygen shortage and other problems was critical to their survival. Had he been on Apollo 13 he would not have had a chance to experience a successful space mission. Instead, he replaced Swigert on the successful Apollo 16 lunar landing mission with LM Pilot Charlie Duke and Commander John Young. God looked out for Ken Mattingly after all.

18. *Corrective Action*

The ground team's and contractors' elation and celebrations over our success in getting the Apollo 13 crew back safely quickly subsided. NASA and Rockwell, the prime contractor for the Command and Service Module, had to find and fix the problem that caused the oxygen tank to explode or we would never have another Apollo flight. In addition, we who supported the flight controllers took on the task of looking for any other latent problems that might be lurking. We did not need any more unpleasant surprises. The lives of the flight crew and the nation's manned space program depended on us.

The day after the Apollo 13 splashdown NASA convened a Review Board of experts. In two months they issued their report. A combination of mistakes and a less-than-robust design had caused the explosion. The oxygen tank (manufactured by a Rockwell subcontractor, Beach Aircraft) contained two inadequate protective thermostatic switches on the heater assembly. The test procedures of this system, after connecting with the spacecraft, caused tank overheating at Cape Kennedy (now Cape Canaveral) prior to launch, without detection by the protective switches. Inadequate preflight testing procedures on the switches left their flaw undiscovered. At fifty-six hours into the Apollo 13 mission, a short circuit in a wiring conduit for the tank heater caused the oxygen tank to overheat to 1,000 degrees and explode. The switches failed to open, thereby allowing the overheating to take place. Rockwell and its subcontractors—under NASA direction—implemented a series of detailed corrective measures. These enabled Apollo 14 to be scheduled for a January 31, 1971 launch just nine months after the accident targeted to the same landing site, Fra Mauro, originally planned for Apollo 13. I doubt this could ever be accomplished in today's bureaucratic environment, where it took years to get the Shuttle back on track after its catastrophic problems.

My alignment with this quest for perfection in the equipment and the mission rules drove me to rewrite the flight software and support software perhaps 100 times, retesting and improving it each time, in my two year assignment at MIT. When I left there in 1967 and turned my software over to the maintenance team, I truly believed I'd made the best possible achievement with the 1960's flight computer hardware that would fly on the LM and Command Modules. Since it was ultimately used in all Apollo flights, as well as the subsequent Skylab and Apollo/Soyuz missions with virtually no change during those eight years, I felt satisfied I had accomplished my objective.

Now, as Section Head at TRW, I had taken on additional responsibilities to those supporting the Apollo missions. I had one team continuing to verify the lunar ascent and descent guidance and navigation software and its changes. Another continued to support mission planning by modifying the full six-degrees-of-freedom simulation of the elements of both spacecrafts, the Saturn launch vehicle, and the earth-moon environment. In addition, I persuaded NASA to task us to develop a computer program to support the planning of the "Grand Tour" Mission.

The Grand Tour was to take advantage of a once-in-a-lifetime opportunity to visit all the outer planets in the solar system with a single mission. During the next decade Mars, Jupiter, Saturn, and Uranus would be perfectly aligned to enable a spacecraft to get a "gravity assist" from each planet. As an object passes close to a planet, it actually picks up energy relative to inertial space, according to the planet's speed. By passing the planet in the same direction the planet is moving relative to the sun, it picks up the planet's speed. By designing the perfect trajectory, we could visit all these planets—maybe even Pluto—using fuel only to make minor corrections to the trajectory.

NASA needed a new sophisticated computer program to simulate this mission to accurately model the gravitational field of each planet, its atmosphere (if any), and the gravitational attraction of any natural satellites. It also had to model the forces of the solar wind and any other phenomena in the solar system that could exert force on a freely floating spacecraft. We would design our program much like the one used for the earth-moon mission, but would introduce all these solar system forces which were almost negligible—and therefore ignored—for Apollo. For the majority of the Grand Tour mission, these forces are small compared to the Sun's gravity so we were able to start with the approximation of an elliptical trajectory orbiting the sun, and then integrate the various forces as perturbations to this approximation. We had to develop a more efficient numerical integration algorithm in order to compute these multi-year trajectories in a reasonable amount of computer time. This was not my expertise, so I hired a numerical integration expert. When the spacecraft was relatively far from the planets and their natural satellites, the perturbations from the elliptical orbit around the sun were small, enabling us to take large time-steps (hours) in the numerical integration algorithm that computed the deviations from the ellipse.

Because we would start with the basic structure of the much simpler Apollo navigation program hosted on the ground mainframe computers, we had to first document and understand the Apollo program completely. IBM developed and modified the existing program on NASA's mainframe IBM computers outside the Mission Control Room. But the documentation was significantly out of date and contained errors in some cases. We discovered these errors as we decoded the actual listings of the program code and created flow charts of how the programs really worked. Most of the errors were in the documentation rather than the software itself. Otherwise they would likely have been detected during the test and training phases, and would have then been fixed. It would be rare, but not impossible, to encounter such errors during the real mission. However, I discovered one error in the actual software that would have resulted in the spacecraft's computed velocity to be erroneous garbage (almost twice the correct value). Had the obscure option to invoke this part of the flawed code been used in real time during a mission, the ground system would have lost the ability to support the mission until corrected by the flight software.

Of course I immediately reported this to our NASA manager, who relayed it to the ground support staff. Even though we documented how to fix the error in the FORTRAN code, NASA had a problem in getting IBM to implement the correction. The code change was not the problem, but rather the verification that the change did not affect something else in the vast array of real-time ground support programs on which the flight controllers had to rely. IBM's policy was that any time a change is made to any part of the real-time ground programs, they had to repeat the months of testing to verify and validate that all the software worked. Thus, my discovery, in the aftermath of Apollo 13, became a "worry item."

After Apollo 13, TRW—like many other NASA contractors —instituted a Worry Item List. Any TRW employee, who believed a relevant problem might exist to jeopardize the success or safety of the next mission, reported it to a TRW committee headed by the local TRW General Manager, Clarence Pittman. The committee would investigate each problem to either conclude it was not of concern, or report it to NASA management at a visible level. My finding was one of a handful to make it to NASA through this high-level vetting chain. NASA finally mitigated the problem, not by ordering the code change, but by issuing a new mission rule mandating that this option in the program never be used.

Meanwhile the flight crew was growing impatient for their Apollo 14 mission. They had been training for more than two years. The Apollo

13 failure had added some new contingency training to their schedule but, like all the Apollo astronauts, they were more than eager to get on with the mission. Although all the astronauts had their own different individual personalities and interests, the common thread was their burning desire to get into space as the top priority. The Apollo 14 crew consisted of veteran astronaut Alan Shepard (at age forty-seven dubbed the "old man" by the other astronauts) and rookies Stu Roosa and Ed Mitchell. Shepard, a member of the famed Original Mercury Seven, was America's first man in space when he flew the sub-orbital Mercury mission in 1961. He, with Deke Slayton, served as Chief of the Astronaut Office. Although Sue and I met him in the Astronaut Viewing Area at the Apollo 11 launch, we didn't know him. Known as the rich astronaut, who gained his wealth through stock market investments, he had moved to the upscale part of Houston's River Oaks subdivision, where every home looked like a mansion.

I think he was the only astronaut who did not live in one of the four towns surrounding the Johnson Space Center: Clear Lake City, Timber Cove, Nassau Bay, and our own El Lago.

The Apollo 14 mission was a complete success by every measure. But I remember it best for something Shepard did, which enhanced my opinion of him. Each astronaut who landed on the moon was allowed to carry a limited amount (no more than one pound) of personal items with him to the lunar surface. Shepard, an excellent golfer, brought two golf balls and a collapsible 6-iron. He actually demonstrated the low lunar gravity and lack of atmosphere by hitting the golf ball (even in his bulky spacesuit) "miles and miles," as he was quoted. I loved it.

Alan Shepard graduated from the US Naval Academy in Annapolis in 1944 and retired from NASA and the Navy as a Rear Admiral in 1974. At age seventy-four, he died of leukemia on my birthday in 1998 in Pebble Beach, California.

19. *"Goodbye, Mr. Duke"*

Charlie and Dotty Duke moved to Texas from California where Charlie had been an instructor at the Test Pilot School at Edwards AFB. The Dukes' children were the same ages as our two: Charles–two and Tom–a baby. Our kids became best friends, and we and the Dukes became mutual second parents for each other. Whenever the Dukes needed someone to take care of Charles and Tom, we did so, and they reciprocated. Their opportunities to get away were more exciting than ours, such as the Indy 500. Also, our respective parents, living in other parts of the country, were always welcomed into our neighborhood gatherings whenever they visited. We came to know Dotty's parents well. Dotty's father was a small southern gentleman with a warm personality, which may have been honed by his career as a physician in Atlanta.

We often let off steam and partied together. Being young and foolish, we sometimes had too much to drink at these neighborhood parties. I particularly remember one at the Dukes' home. Charlie had invited most of his astronaut buddies, some key NASA people, and top executives of the local companies. One of the NASA guests, Bill Tindal (the NASA leader at MIT/IL), warned Sue and me at the door to "be careful of the punch." It seemed innocuous enough, and tasted mild and good. It flowed in a never-ending waterfall from several spouts in a silver fountain on the table. It was just too easy to stand there socializing, eating hors d'oeuvres and refilling one's glass, until I noticed that the room seemed to be listing. I remember the difficulty of navigating the 100 yards across their back yard to our home. The next day we all gave Charlie a hard time for spiking the punch with 151-proof rum.

Charlie was selected as a NASA astronaut in the fifth class, and thus was a relative rookie in 1967. But, like all the astronauts we knew, he lived for the opportunity to soar into space. Nothing was more important to him. It was clear to me that he would make it. His pleasant personality and South Carolina southern drawl combined with his excellent intellectual abilities and ambitious drive to produce the perfect astronaut, especially to the external world. He was a graduate of the Naval Academy but commissioned in the Air Force at Graduation to begin pilot training. He earned a master's degree in aeronautics and astronautics from MIT. As all the other pioneering astronauts, he was a top test pilot. Still, he respected my MIT background in astronautics and my accomplishments with developing the Apollo flight software. But Charlie had a way of making everyone feel important. That, together with his abilities, vaulted him to the forefront in competing for the best assignments. He was one of the three CAPCOMs for the first lunar landing mission and got his first 15 minutes of international fame as he talked down Neil Armstrong and Buzz Aldrin on their exciting and dangerous descent to the moon. He reported that they had less than 30 seconds of fuel left and was ready to relay the command to ABORT when they finally touched down. After Armstrong said, "The eagle has landed." Charlie quipped "You got a bunch of guys here about to turn blue. We're breathing again. Thanks a lot." If you visit the Smithsonian Air and Space Museum, you can hear this quote from Charlie.

As backup LM pilot for Apollo 13, Charlie played an important role on the ground during the Apollo 13 accident. With the rest of the ground crew, he helped develop lifesaving crew procedures on the ground-based simulator that were used by the Apollo 13 crew to return safely.

As expected after Apollo 13 returned, and NASA made the decision to cut back to only four more lunar missions, Mattingly, Young, and Duke (pictured below) were named as the primary crew for Apollo 16, scheduled for April, 1972. As a lesson learned from the measles issue, all future primary crews were to go into quarantine three weeks prior to the scheduled launch. From this point on, Charlie's sole role

was to train for his mission to Descartes in the lunar highlands. However, when I noticed an oscillation during the final seconds of lunar descent from my guidance software verification work using TRW's digital simulation of the lunar module, I asked Charlie to check it out on NASA's simulator. I had reported my concern to TRW top management but they had little success in getting NASA's attention to the problem. Charlie confirmed the oscillation instability, but it was not as pronounced as shown by our results. Since the crew was to override the primary guidance commands during the last 500 feet of descent, the problem would never be encountered as long as the crew followed the flight control procedures. This is why the anomaly hadn't been seen on previous flights.

After the successful Apollo 14 and 15 missions, preparations were proceeding for the Apollo 16 launch. Charlie managed to get a pass for my whole family to view the launch from the parkway along the Banana River—not far from the Vehicle Assembly Building and the bleachers where the dignitaries would view the launch. This was less than a mile from our vantage point for the Apollo 11 launch. I received permission from TRW for the time off and we drove to Cape Kennedy (now Cape Canaveral). Once again we stayed with our friends and former neighbors, the

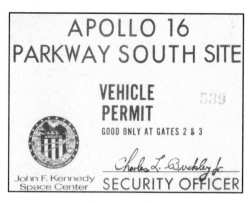

Gilberts. Rom was working at the launch control center, so we had his wife Lois and their kids pile into our car to use the pass and see the launch. It was beautiful and went right on schedule. I wasn't sure that our daughter Sheryl was old enough (just turned five) to understand what was going on, until she waved as the Saturn majestically roared off into the atmosphere and said "Goodbye, Mr. Duke."

But Charlie's mission did not go smoothly. The crew had named the CM *Casper* and the LM *Orion*. After successfully entering lunar orbit, Charlie and John donned their spacesuits in the weightless environment and crawled through the tunnel from *Casper* to *Orion* to start the undocking. But drops of orange juice from a leaky valve in Charlie's drink bag tube began floating in his helmet. It coated his visor and settled into his hair—a minor but frustrating problem. (After landing, the juice clogged his microphone, forcing him to remove his helmet to clean it before exiting the LM.) Then a more serious problem occurred. The antenna for the primary communications link to Houston would not rotate in one direction, resulting in a poor link and preventing data uplink from the ground. As a result Charlie had to enter the required data updates (thirty-five 5-digit numbers) into the *Orion* computer. Then there was a pressure malfunction in the *Orion* primary attitude control system, which they fixed by venting pressure into *Orion*'s ascent stage fuel tank. They received the "GO" to undock from *Casper*, which would occur on the back side of the moon. But a worse problem occurred on the far side of the moon after *Orion* separated from *Casper*. One hour before *Orion* was supposed to begin descent, Mattingly reported a major problem with *Casper*'s main engine's backup control system. Redundancy rules required that both the primary and secondary systems be operational before *Orion* began descent. *Casper* had to achieve a circular orbit enabling *Orion*'s rendezvous after ascent from the moon. Yaw oscillations of the propulsion system could have prevented a go for landing, forcing an abort decision. But Mission Control developed a workaround while they continued to orbit the moon, enabling the landing six hours late.

The rest of the landing went without a hitch, missing their Descartes landing site target by less than 300 yards. Charlie and John were exhilarated exploring the lunar surface, collecting rocks, and performing experiments. The lunar highlands terrain was rugged with giant craters and large rocks likely expended from the meteorite collisions over the past four billion years.

They spent more than twenty hours driving around in their lunar rover over their three-day stay on the moon. This gave them much more ability to explore than previous Apollo missions. They were able to make excursions of up to ten miles from the LM. They were like kids, driving the rover up to 7 mph, bouncing up and down on the rough terrain in unearthly lunar gravity

and loving every minute. Charlie's book, *Moonwalker*, does a great job describing their explorations in detail. Three days after the landing they blasted off in the ascent stage with their cargo of 216 pounds of rocks (which weighed only 36 pounds on the moon), leaving the descent stage and rover on the moon, and rendezvoused with *Casper*. We experienced much of this with Dotty at the Duke's home, listening to the "squawk box."

Once docked, they transferred to *Casper* with their cargo, jettisoned *Orion*, and lit *Casper*'s main engine for the return home. After successfully negotiating the most dangerous part of the mission, reentry into the earth's atmosphere, they splashed down in the Pacific Ocean. Initially the CM was upside down in the Pacific, but floatation balloons were deployed to right the spacecraft. They were fished out by helicopter and placed on the deck of the *Ticonderoga*.

The next day we went to Elington AFB to welcome the crew return to Houston. Then we helped them celebrate at the Dukes' home.

When Charlie returned, he brought us the above mosaic of memorabilia, which he had mounted for us. It included the Apollo 16 logo; the flag of Texas (which he had taken down to the moon's surface); and a picture of him on the moon saluting—with the Lunar Module in the background, taken by Commander John Young, and a personal inscription: "A big salute to Sue and Kurth, two wonderful friends and neighbors. With sincere best wishes, (signed) Charlie Duke." As you can see above, the sun has faded his inscription to almost illegible in the past forty-five years. He also gave Sue a pendent of the Apollo 16 emblem that he had carried to Descartes, their landing site. The inscription on the back reads "to Sue from Charlie via Descartes." Charlie also left a picture of his family on the moon.

Charlie is a good golfer with a single digit handicap. Ben Hogan played with him several times. When he returned from the moon, Hogan gave him a bag and a set of clubs made by Hogan's company with the Apollo 16 logo on each club as well as the bag. They were beautiful. But Hogan said he would never do that again. He had to discard hundreds of irons forged with the logo imbedded, before they were right. Charlie played with me at my country club's annual Hurricane Tournament. We didn't win, but Charlie played well and bet on us.

The Dukes moved from El Lago a few months after we did. Charlie and his silent partner were successful in a competition with 300 applicants and were awarded one of the four new Coors Beer distributorships: theirs was in San Antonio. They moved to New Braunfels, Texas to manage this wonderful business opportunity and made it a big success. Charlie comfortably retired two years later but still resides in New Braunfels.

He also retired as a Brigadier General, and was recruiting for the Air Force Academy when our son, Scott had a decision to make. Scott had been awarded an early appointment to the Military Academy at West Point, but had not yet received an early appointment to the Air Force Academy. At my request, Charlie, who was like a second father to Scott in El Lago, called Scott and convinced him to wait for the Air Force, even if he had to turn down the West Point appointment. Scott accepted the AFA appointment one day before the West Point expiration date.

Charlie and Dotty are now international speakers, traveling around the world. Charlie speaks about his Apollo 16 adventure, and they also give their testimony on their return to Christ. They have visited us many times over the years. After promising to visit them, we finally spent a few days in their home in 2009. Their house looked like a museum with Apollo and Air Force memorabilia throughout. Also big game hunters, they likewise displayed several impressive mounted animal busts. They took us to a western hoedown, the New Braunfels annual Wurstfest, and I learned they were good dancers. After Buzz Aldrin made a fool of himself on "Dancing with the Stars," I implored Charlie to get on the show to prove astronauts can dance, but he never took me up on it.

In 2013, Charlie and Dotty invited us to join them for Charlie's induction into the International Air & Space Museum in San Diego. We enjoyed the black-tie affair held at the museum. We also got reacquainted with one of my customers in the 1980s, inductee Glynn Lunney of NASA's Mission Control Team. And we met "Sully" Sullenberger, the Captain of the Airbus 320 who made the heroic emergency landing on the Hudson River saving all 155 passengers and crew ("The Miracle on the Hudson"). Sully's entire crew was inducted into the Hall of Fame.

20. *Apollo 17—The End of an Era*

Congress voted to cut NASA's funding for 1972, forcing the cancellation of Apollo 18, 19, and 20. In December Apollo 17 would be the last of that glorious time when Americans walked (and rode) on the moon. The crew selections: our neighbor and friend, Ron Evans—the Command Module Pilot; veteran Gene

Cernan—the mission Commander, and the first scientist/geologist astronaut, Harrison "Jack" Schmitt—Lunar Module Pilot. John Young, Stu Roosa, and Charlie Duke, all veterans of previous Apollo lunar landings made up the backup crew.

For the last time, we once again erected the large wooden American Flag with the red, white, and blue Christmas tree bulbs on Evans' front lawn (just one door down from our El Lago home on Woodland Drive). Our kids had grown up together. We wanted to give Ron a good send-off. We did, indeed.

Each crew member had to go into quarantine several days prior to launch to minimize his exposure to disease which might exclude him from the mission. We neighbors decided to have a bon voyage party in our home the night before Ron had to leave for quarantine. Since Ron was always a fun-loving cut-up, we planned something special. First, we got into the Evans house the day before the party and planted a speaker above his master bedroom connected to wires strung through the attic and across to a neighbor's house. The night of the party we all brought gag gifts and cards appropriately reflecting Ron's last night to be spent alone with his wife, Jan. Their kids stayed with friends and neighbors. Ron and Jan loved the "gifts" and had a good laugh, but they didn't realize the best fun was yet to come.

All went home rather early and met at the home where the microphone was connected to the speaker. We waited a sufficiently long time, and then we started. With romantic music playing in the background we complimented Ron and Jan on their wonderful performance. They didn't realize that although they could hear us, we could not hear them ... it was not a two-way communication system. We continued to tease the couple for a few minutes, and then we quietly returned to our respective homes for the night. The next morning Sue and I awakened at dawn to see Ron pointing a shotgun at us as we lay in bed. He still had some fiberglass in his hair apparently from rummaging around his attic, looking for the microphone. Jan was filming us with a NASA video camera. I have no idea how they got into our house. You could say they appropriately got back at us.

Later that day we all gathered at Ellington AFB to see Ron off for his flight to the Cape and his quarantine quarters. After we said our good-byes and began waving our American flags, Ron got into the pilot seat of his white T-38 two-person jet that all the astronauts used for transportation. He started the dual engines and began taxiing down the runway. Suddenly he made a sharp right turn and headed for us! The needle nose of the T-38 was pointed directly at us and seemed awfully close before he veered back on the runway and took off. Many of our astronaut neighbors sometimes enjoyed buzzing our houses when they returned from the Cape prior to landing at Ellington, but none ever got that close.

The Apollo 17 launch on December 7th was spectacular, because they launched at night for the first time. Although formally invited, we did not see it in person; those that did were impressed. The mission was another outstanding success. While Ron kept the Command Module in a circular orbit sixty-nine miles above the lunar surface, Cernan and Schmitt explored the Taurus-Littrow Valley. They gathered 243 pounds (weight on earth, but 40 pounds on the moon) of moon rocks and core samples during three separate excursions with the lunar rover during their three-day stay. This area contained boulders near the base of small mountains, with evidence of a landslide, impact craters, and dark craters probably caused by volcanoes. They also left several sensors for gathering and transmitting seismic and chemical data back to earth. Prior to lifting off on December 14, 1972, Cernan was quoted: "As I take man's last step from the surface, back home for some time to come—but we believe not too long into the future—I'd like to just [say] what I believe history will record—that America's challenge of today has forged man's destiny of tomorrow. And, as we leave the Moon at Taurus-Littrow, we leave as we came and, God willing, as we shall return, with peace and hope for all mankind. Godspeed the crew of Apollo 17."

The Lunar Module's ascent stage explosively ignited and rapidly accelerated upward, leaving on the lunar surface the descent stage with its plaque commemorating the American crew's last visit to the moon. It read "Here Man completed his first explorations of the moon. December 1972 AD. May the spirit of peace in which we came be reflected in the lives of all mankind." The plaque showed two hemispheres of Earth and the facing side of the Moon, plus the signatures of Cernan, Evans, Schmitt, and President Nixon.

They rendezvoused flawlessly with Ron's Command Module, docked, and transferred through the docking tunnel. They jettisoned the ascent stage in lunar orbit. Ron ignited the Service Module engine and accelerated for the trip home. During the trans-earth coast, Ron did an Extravehicular Activity (EVA) to retrieve the film from the Sim Bay Camera. They splashed down 400 miles southeast of the Samoan Islands, just four miles from the aircraft carrier *Ticonderoga*, their recovery ship. After being fished out of the ocean, they were flown to Samoa, then Honolulu, and finally back to Houston, receiving an ovation at each stop. They had broken several records: the longest manned lunar landing mission; longest total lunar surface EVA; largest lunar sample return, and longest time in lunar orbit.

Like many of the astronauts, Ron enjoyed capturing the excitement in a book.

But the return was bittersweet for me. It was sad to see the greatest achievement of our space program come to an end.

Oh, we would go on to have three successful Skylab missions and the Apollo-Soyuz docking with the Soviets. We would also achieve some success with the Shuttle and Space Station Programs. But this was an era that would never return. America needed success after the negative decade of the 60s and what better way to provide it than the achievements of the Apollo Program. The entire Apollo program cost $25 billion. We will achieve more in the future, but never with the zeal, talent, courage, and dedication of these true pioneers. I have been so fortunate to be part of it.

Seventeen years later, we were invited to and attended the week-long 20th anniversary of the moon landing at JSC in Houston. I enjoyed renewing old acquaintances and reminiscing. At the gala ball the final night, all the

astronauts were invited to say a few words. Although their speeches were typically only 2-3 minutes each, some were quite eloquent.

We hope to attend the 50th anniversary in 2019.

21. *After Apollo*

I received a promotion to Section Head, then Assistant Department Manager and, finally, Department Manager in the three years after Apollo. TRW's contract supporting NASA's Mission Planning Division continued for the three Skylab Missions in 1973-4, followed by the Apollo/Soyuz Mission in 1975. Our neighbor, Jerry Carr was the Commander on the third and last Skylab Mission, the only rookie selected to command an Apollo mission. He originally was supposed to fly to the moon on Apollo 18, but it was cancelled. Jerry, like our other neighbors, wrote a book about his eighty-four days in space. Once again, we received a formal invitation to view the launch, but declined.

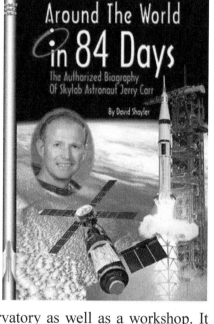

Skylab was a 170,000-pound space station launched in 1973 into near-earth orbit. It included a solar observatory as well as a workshop. It

was the precursor to the giant permanent International Space Station for the 21st century. Even though these launches reached only near-earth orbit, it still took a Saturn V to launch Skylab because of its weight. The three manned missions, with the Apollo CSMs as the payload, were launched with the smaller Saturn S1-B booster.

Skylab was electrically powered with solar panels. But one was damaged during launch. On the first mission, the crew (Pete Conrad, physician Joe Kerwin, and rookie Paul Wietz) was able to deploy a replacement heat shade, designed by our NASA neighbor, Bill Huber, thus saving the program. We learned much about the sun and the earth from Skylab's thousands of photographs. In 1979, NASA caused the spent Skylab to burn up in the earth's atmosphere. My team supported the planning for each mission. But by that time, as I was now a Department Manager, my hands-on engineering work had come to an end. My job had evolved into managing managers, satisfying customers, maximizing profits, and developing new business.

The final flight of the Apollo spacecraft took place in July 1975. Therefore this was the last time my navigation, rendezvous, and return-to-earth targeting software would be used. President Richard Nixon wanted this mission to show cooperation with the Soviet Union in hopes of mitigating the cold war, although Nixon had resigned before the mission commenced. Apollo/Soyuz was the first joint mission with the Russians. Each country would launch its own spacecraft, then dock together to conduct joint experiments. I sent a team

of three engineers to Moscow to support the mission from the Soviet control center. We learned, although the Soviet Union had great expertise in building booster rockets, they were well behind us in computers and control systems. We finally ordered them to just keep their Soyuz spacecraft stable and we would perform all the rendezvous and docking maneuvers. We also discovered that the Soviet ground controllers were not nearly as disciplined and knowledgeable as ours. Deke Slayton, the last of the original Mercury Seven astronauts, finally made it into space for the first time on Apollo/Soyuz. He joined Commander, Tom Stafford,

rookie, Vance Brand, and two cosmonauts for this mission.

Once we convinced the Soviets to keep the Soyuz passive, with the Apollo CSM the active vehicle, the mission went smoothly, until the final phase. After jettisoning the Service Module and beginning entry into the atmosphere, a loud buzzing in one of the switches in the Command Module distracted the crew, causing Brand not to hear Stafford's command to close the valve to the reaction control jets. This caused highly toxic nitrous oxide gas to invade the CM chamber. By the time Stafford and Slayton realized they were becoming asphyxiated and had donned oxygen masks, Brand had passed out. Stafford forced the mask on him just in time, saving his life. If they all had passed out, they would have perished because they could not have deployed the main parachutes and

GUEST INVITATION

APOLLO SOYUZ
TEST PROJECT

NASA / CONTRACTOR
MANNED FLIGHT AWARENESS

Reception

Gilruth Center
JSC-Houston, Texas

6 to 8 pm
July 18, 1975

would have hit the water at 400 mph. Even the splashdown was not nominal, as the CM was upside down in the water. It was righted when the floatation balloons activated. All three astronauts were hospitalized for two weeks to recover from the inhalation. How fitting that the last of the Apollo missions would end so dramatically.

Afterward, I was invited to attend a reception to celebrate the success of the final Apollo mission.

As the Apollo Program wound down, NASA encouraged TRW to do its part in regard to public relations for their programs. The luster was waning with both the politicians and the public, and concern rose about funding cuts. Wisconsin's Badger Boy's State, which I attended as a high school junior in 1957, somehow heard about my achievements and asked TRW to send me there to speak at their evening session. They happily complied. I delivered a forty-five-minute address about my role in the Apollo Program to the 700 high school juniors at Ripon College. Some were probably bored, but at least fifty stayed afterward to ask

PROMINENT BADGER BOYS STATE ALUMNI
Scott K. Walker (1985) - Milwaukee County Executive and Former State House of Representatives (Wisconsin)
(James) Scott McCallum (1967) - Former Governor, State of Wisconsin
Llyod Solberg (1965) - Prominent Cardiologist M.D.,Ph.D
Thomas Hefty (1964) - C.E.O. Blue Cross & Blue Shield United of Wisconsin
Gus Gnorski (1962) - Milwaukee TV6 Personality (Governor BBS)
Robert E. Behling (1958) - Professor of Geology & Geography, Published author of numerous publications and Geology Lab. Manuals
Dan Travanti (1957) - Actor
Lee W. Huebner (1957) - One of the founders of Ripon Society. Speech writer, special assistant to President Nixon. Publisher International Herald Tribune
Kurth W. Krause (1957) - Physicist with Apollo (Voice giving instructions for landing on the moon) NASA Achievement Award 1969.
Al Jarreau (1957) - Renowned Jazz Singer (Governor)
Thomas E. Petri (1957) - U.S. House of Representatives since 1979
Martin J. Schreiber (1956) - Former Governor, State of Wisconsin
Wm. Steiger (1955) - Elected U.S. Congressman at age of 28; deceased while in office (Governor)
Jon G. Udell (1952) - University of Wisconsin-Madison Irwin Maier Professor of Business Graduate School
Bruce Hapke (1948) - Principal investigator for study of Apollo Lunar Samples, member of early imaging science team.
Pete Stark (1948) - Served as U.S. Congressman from California
Robert G. Froehlke (1939) - Former Secretary of the Army, Pres., Health Insurance Assoc. of America
Donald G. Iselin: Rear Admiral (1939) - Distinguished U.S. Naval Engineering Career; Named Commander, Naval Facilities Eng. & Chief Civil Engrs.

me questions. They were excited about the program and that "one of their own" had made a contribution. As a result I am now on the list of prominent BBS alumni, along with governors, congressmen, and entertainers.

I also was interviewed on Wisconsin TV and radio programs, which I enjoyed. I felt like a celebrity, while presenting to the public the value of NASA's programs. With the help of NASA's public relations team, I compiled a list of dozens of practical benefits the public had received from the programs, especially Apollo. Of course there were also the scientific benefits, such as learning from the composition of the moon rocks that the moon was likely formed from a meteor collision with a molten earth. But most people were interested in the everyday benefits to their lives, such as Velcro, invented to keep objects from freefalling inside the spacecraft. Today the most valuable practical benefit is likely the great leaps of progress in computer technology and software forged by the Apollo Program.

I sent my list to Paul Harvey, the world-famous commentator for ABC, who had a daily radio program that reached as many as twenty-four million listeners each week. I was delighted when he filled his fifteen minute broadcast with my list. He presented it in a much more interesting style than I ever could have. Harvey was awarded the Presidential Medal of Freedom in 2005, four years before his death at age 90. *"And that's the rest of the story."*

22. *Space Shuttle Program—The Competitive Phase*

Before the highly successful Apollo and Skylab Programs wound down in 1975, NASA launched its next big step in space—the Shuttle Transportation System (STS) Program. They reasoned that for man to have continuous access to space, the country needed a low-cost launch and recovery system that could be used routinely. The objective: to be able to launch and land in a "shirtsleeve" capsule at 10 percent of the cost of the Saturn delivery system. The capsule environment would be closer to that of today's airliners: safe, low G forces, and would land at an airfield similar to an airplane. One of the "requirements" (only partially jokingly): the occupants would not "spill their coffee" during the launch phase or even the jolting reentry into the earth's atmosphere.

The Shuttle would have several missions:

1. Launch, deploy, repair, and retrieve satellites in low (approximately 200-400 miles) earth orbit

2. Build a permanent space station that astronauts could use en route to the planets

3. Determine man's ability to successfully function for long time periods in space

4. Perform myriad science experiments in the weightless, near-vacuum of space

In early 1972 Clarence Pittman, who headed our 1,000 person TRW Houston office, decided to explore a Shuttle software integration subcontractor role. He selected me (a lowly Section Head at the time) to help him sell the idea. McDonnell Douglas Aerospace Corporation (MDAC) in St. Louis was competing with Rockwell International and Grumman Corporation for the prize Shuttle contract to build the orbiter. TRW in Redondo Beach had teamed with MDAC as the orbiter avionics subcontractor. TRW/Houston had no role. Pittman wanted to convince John Yardley, MDAC's Executive Vice President, that NASA and MDAC needed a contractor like TRW to coordinate (integrate) the development of all Shuttle software for the orbiter, the ground system, and the simulators. This would involve imposing standards and procedures for all software contractors to follow and to provide the oversight to ensure proper implementation. I enjoyed helping Pittman develop the pitch to Yardley, and got to fly first class for the first time and dine at Houston's best restaurant, since I traveled with Pittman ... my first taste of the perks of an executive. (I could get used to this—no problem!) When Yardley decided against our idea, we sold it to NASA. They added it temporarily to our Apollo support contract as a new project. I led the role to develop the software standards that NASA would impose on all contractors at NASA Headquarters in Virginia, at the Marshall Space Flight Center in Alabama, at Kennedy Space Center in Florida, and at the Johnson Space Center in Texas. My job included convincing each NASA organization and their contractors to accept and implement these standards.

In late 1972 TRW/Houston competed to develop the software for the Shuttle ground control system but lost to IBM. This was not a surprise since IBM Federal Systems had been the primary software developer for all the Apollo, Skylab, and Apollo Soyuz ground computers. Some at TRW believed that we put in a bid at NASA's request just to make sure that IBM had someone credible to compete against. I was responsible for writing a key section of the proposal on the software development process we would use. This exposed my work to the senior TRW management team from our California headquarters that reviewed our proposal and singled out my section for praise. NASA also liked it.

In 1973 TRW had to compete for a new support contract for the Shuttle era—a similar role to our Apollo/Skylab contract. Based on past performance on the Apollo/Skylab contracts, no competitor was close. NASA was ecstatic with the work we had done the previous nine years, and most believed no one had a chance to unseat us. But Chris Kraft, now Director of JSC, was angry that TRW took financial advantage of our top performance. We not only earned 12 to 14 percent award fees on the contracts with NASA, but we were charging the same overhead rate set by our more costly space and defense corporate headquarters in Redondo Beach, California. Therefore NASA was paying the same overhead rate we charged our military customers for building and testing expensive highly classified military satellites. Kraft was furious that we would not voluntarily reduce our rates to the highly competitive low rates required to compete in the recessionary aerospace environment in Houston in the early 1970s. He made no secret of this in trying to persuade competitors to bid against us for the STS support contract. One contractor gave it a try: MDAC.

MDAC had nothing to lose; winning this contract from TRW was the only way to stay alive at JSC. Their work on Apollo and Skylab was winding down to nothing. They had laid off or transferred all but thirty people of the hundreds they needed a few years ago. John Yardley orchestrated their competition. If they lost, the remaining thirty had a choice: be laid off or pay their own way back to St. Louis for reassignment. If they won, these thirty would become the top management for the new Shuttle support contract and could keep their homes in Houston.

But TRW got the message—at least partially. Pittman created a new local cost center, cutting our overhead to rates below what we could likely meet. No longer would the west-coast headquarters be annually subsidized with $1 million of excess overhead cash paid for by our NASA contracts. But ... we lost!

I was on a plane, unfortunately seated next to John Yardley, just two weeks later. I had to sit there and listen to his boastful tale on how he outsmarted and beat us. MDAC's price was 25 percent lower than ours. While we cut our facility space in half, he proposed just sixty square feet of office space per engineer! While we proposed using our existing staff at their current salaries, he proposed hiring fifty of our lead engineers at a 10 percent cut in salary, while hiring two hundred new college graduates at 15 percent below the going average rate. He planned to use the TRW lead engineers to train the college kids. Then he bid a maximum award fee of 6 percent (to be split with the employees), while we bid the 15 percent we had enjoyed in our previous contracts.

MDAC could not deliver on this aggressive proposal, but it was plausible enough to win. And Kraft wanted to teach us (and the rest of the contractors) a lesson. The result was interesting. MDAC succeeded in hiring only four TRW people and only one of these had any experience as a lead engineer. Despite the recession, MDAC could not hire the new college grads, and received a dispensation from NASA to raise their salary offers to the going rate. Even at that they ended up hiring the lower end of the graduating classes. These kids knew nothing. So the NASA veterans had to do their jobs while training them, quite a different situation from what the NASA engineers had become accustomed to when TRW had done much of the work. Yet NASA couldn't give MDAC the failure award fee grades they deserved, because not only would it demoralize the MDAC employees but it would also advertise that the award to MDAC had been a mistake. But in the long run this worked out well. The NASA engineers had to revitalize their work and use their skills. And eventually the new MDAC employees learned enough to be productive, although they never achieved the proficiency of the TRW veterans.

TRW requested and received a debriefing from NASA explaining why we lost. Our Vice President, Bob Walquist, came to Houston from Redondo Beach to hear the debriefing. Walquist was an imposing figure of a man: 6 feet 6 inches, over two hundred pounds, fifty-something, with an intimidating handshake, and a personality to match. By contrast, the NASA lead briefer, Ron Berry, was a soft-spoken, small man in his forties. Ron had been a colleague of mine since my MIT days ... a nice guy, personable and competent, but new in such an important job of leading the Source Selection Team for one of the first major Shuttle competitions. Ron proceeded to describe the source selection process in detail, explaining why we received grades appropriate in every category of technical, management, past performance, and cost. Clearly we had beaten MDAC in every other category, but had lost on cost. Walquist listened patiently (fuming) until Ron came to the fee. When Ron implied that our fee (compared to MDAC) was "excessive," Walquist stopped him, rose to his full six-six height (probably seemed like ten feet to Ron) and began a loud soliloquy on how NASA needs to learn that fee (profit) is what makes businesses survive. I didn't know anyone could talk to a customer the way Walquist did. But then, I suppose he felt NASA would not be our customer much longer and used this opportunity to get the rage out of his system.

TRW now had the unpleasant task of reducing our Houston office from approximately eight hundred people to one hundred. We had one year of our contract left to support the joint Apollo/Soyuz docking mission with the Soviet Union. Then the final hundred must disappear unless we could land some new work. And the only game in town at that time would be Shuttle.

TRW announced that no engineer would be laid off involuntarily. By early 1974 the aerospace recession had almost ended. TRW had job openings in California, Washington DC, and small offices around the country. So long as we were willing to relocate, each of the engineers would have a job. If we wished to stay in Houston but were not one of the hundred chosen to remain through the summer of 1975, we would have to resign or be laid off. TRW called in a consultant to coach us in résumé preparation and interviewing. Many resented Pittman when he personally took a job in Washington within a few weeks after the loss, rather than staying around to help us find key roles within TRW.

I was in the process of deciding whether to accept an offer with IBM Federal Systems in Houston or one of several offers with TRW in California, when our new California Director of Operations, Bruce Gordon, asked me to stay in Houston for one more year. I would be promoted to Department Manager, select my Staff of three Section Heads and thirty engineers to fulfill the requirements of the Apollo/Soyuz Mission Planning and Analysis Contract, and try to develop new Shuttle business with NASA to sustain the Houston Operation. Two other departments were challenged with the same objective. I would have two bosses: Laboratory Manager Bill Hugel (a senior manager, too young to retire, who wanted to remain in Houston) for developing the new business and Program Manager Vern Widerquist (a crusty senior manager in his 60s, ready to retire) for contract performance. Excellent contract performance would not be difficult if it were not too late to get the cream of the crop of TRW engineers to stay, but new Shuttle business would be difficult with no obvious STS bidding opportunities looming during the next year. Sue and I had always wanted to live in California and were leaning toward the transfer when I was offered the promotion to stay. I could not turn down the additional responsibility and the pay raise. And the best secretary at TRW (twenty years my senior) requested to work for me. I gladly accepted, and learned what a tremendous value a good secretary can be.

I quickly tackled the job of identifying the engineers I wanted for the job, and offered them the option to join my new department. Although most had completed their interviews with local competitors and with TRW in other parts of the country, I succeeded in persuading over 90 percent of my first choices to stay. Of the hundreds of engineers who had to seek other employment, their job decisions encompassed three nearly equal groups:

1. Transfers to other TRW locations

2. Hiring into an aerospace competitor in Houston (fifty-seven went with IBM)

3. Making a career change with a non-aerospace firm in the Houston area

The lean overhead structure introduced for the new local cost center left no real budget for new business development. But we had something more important—a solid track record of performance by key people who might disappear from the NASA scene after Apollo/Soyuz if we were unsuccessful in obtaining new Shuttle business. The NASA engineers were well aware of this, enabling me to sell Shuttle ideas for my people to perform. The problem was that MDAC and others who won their large STS competitions insisted that our ideas for new work belonged on their new contracts. So we had to perform the work under subcontract to MDAC and others. But I succeeded in meeting the performance and new business objectives.

We earned record performance grades, receiving as much as 100 percent of the possible award fee. This came about partly because my engineers were very competent, and partly because our graders were the same NASA lead engineers who were forced to give the poorly performing MDAC teams grades of 80 percent to avoid embarrassment.

By the time the Apollo/Soyuz mission and our contract came to an end in the summer of 1975, my department had captured enough Shuttle business for the department to grow to fifty people. Unfortunately the other two departments were unsuccessful in capturing any new business and had to dissolve. I began to interview in Redondo Beach for my next TRW assignment and transfer, and succeeded in obtaining six different job offers there. But Bruce Gordon again asked me to stay and run our now small Houston office. Did I want to be a big fish in a small pond? Would this be career limiting since our ability to grow locally would be minimal? After much consternation, I turned him down and accepted a management job on the new TRW $100 million ballistic missile defense software subcontract to MDAC in Huntington Beach, California. Unfortunately, this project was outside Bruce's organization. As a result, I lost a key mentor. This was also the end of my exciting ten year career working on NASA programs ... or so I thought.

So I chose to accept the offer to transfer to LA and manage twenty-five engineers on the new ballistic missile defense program. TRW bought my house in El Lago, paid for a house hunting trip, and moved our belongings and one car. We packed the kids into the second car, a Mercury station wagon (in which the air conditioning conked out before we even left Houston city limits), in August 1975 and set out for a week-long trip through Texas, New Mexico, Arizona, and California, sightseeing all the way. Ten-year-old Scott seemed to enjoy the adventure, but eight-year-old Sheryl did not. She was carsick and slept much of the way. When I woke her up to see the mountains in California, she said, "See one mountain, you've seen 'em all." Naturally the kids were not happy to leave their friends and school. They had attended Ed White Elementary, named in honor of his death in the 1967 Apollo 1 fire. They had received an excellent education there and, as a result, learned nothing new in their first year in California's school system, even though the Newport/Mesa school district was rated one of the best in the state.

23. *Strategic Missile Defense*

The US Strategic Missile Defense Program created my ticket to TRW's aerospace headquarters. TRW won a research and development contract with the US Army as a subcontractor to MDAC in 1973. The objective: to determine whether the technology had matured sufficiently to build a system to defend against a strategic nuclear attack by the Soviet Union by destroying the nuclear warhead inflight before it hit our cities. There were many issues involved in the program, some subtle.

First, could it really be done? Our current Early Warning System of radar sites in Canada might detect a squadron of bombers coming from the Soviet Union, but it would be of no help in detecting and tracking a ballistic missile that could reach our shores in less than thirty minutes. It required a new, space-based surveillance system. A classified system, the Defense Support Program, began in 1970 to solve the early warning detection problem, but it had no capability to destroy the warhead.

Was ground-based radar technology sufficiently advanced to detect a nuclear warhead after its release from the final stage (tank) of the missile delivery system? The tank would break up upon reentry to the atmosphere. Could we distinguish between the pieces of the tank and the nuclear reentry vehicle (RV)? Did we have sufficient computer power to process all the radar data and discriminate between all these pieces detected by the radar, pick out the real RV and track it in sufficient time to pass the target data to an anti-ballistic missile (ABM)? A host of ABMs would be housed near the site for protection from nuclear attack. Could an ABM be fast enough, accurate enough, and lethal enough to destroy a nuclear warhead that reentered the atmosphere at 15,500 miles per hour? All these technology questions had to be solved.

But that was not all. Even if we were able to meet all the technical challenges, the financial and political challenges were equally troubling. Once we spent the money to deploy a defensive system, could the Soviets modify their attacking system with countermeasures to defeat the defense? And could they do it more economically? Could they build cheap decoys to befuddle the radar or the algorithms we derived to discriminate the decoys from the real RVs? Would the computer get bogged down with the complexity of the problem? It had to solve the problem in less than ten seconds to give the ABMs sufficient time to target, launch, and intercept the nuclear warheads. Could the Soviets build a delivery system with multiple warheads per launch vehicle? Could they maneuver, rather than just coast, to increase our tracking difficulty?

The political issue was subtle. Currently most believed the US and USSR had a stable situation: mutually assured destruction. Many argued if we deployed a successful missile defense system, it would destabilize this balance. For this reason, the Army had to change the name of the program from Site Defense to System Technology Program.

Jack Dreyfus had transferred from Houston as a Department Manager and had moved up to Assistant Program Manager under Bob Williams. I reported indirectly to Jack as Subprogram Manager in charge of proving that we had independently verified and validated each of the thousand requirements imposed on the software.

This software was to process the ground-based phased-array radar data, detect the RVs and decoys, discriminate between them, track the real RVs, and issue commands to ground-based ABMs to kill the RVs before they reached their targets. This herculean task had never been done before. In fact, AT&T's Bell Labs had failed trying to solve the same problem to protect our large cities, and declared it could not be done. But we succeeded, earning the respect and maximum award fees from the Army. We had to use two CDC 7600 computers in tandem, sharing a large core memory, which was set up at the Kwajalein atoll in the Pacific with the GE phased-array radars. This was the site used to demonstrate the accomplishment of the missile defense system because it was the site used by our military to test the US RVs launched from Vandenberg Air Force Base. Unfortunately, the Congress had eliminated the ABMs from the program to comply with the ABM treaty with the Soviet Union. The Soviets had convinced our politicians that an effective ABM system would create an imbalance in the concept of assured mutual destruction and would heat up the cold war. Nevertheless, we were able to demonstrate the ability to track the RVs in time to target the (now non-existent) ABMs. So the Program was an amazing success, both technically and managerially. TRW proved something Bell Labs publically stated could not be done, and we earned more than 16 percent award fee in doing so. This was the first stepping stone to President Reagan's Strategic Defense Initiative (SDI) in the late '80s. Popularly known as "Star Wars" by the media and critics, it ultimately contributed to the breakup of the Soviet Union, winning the Cold War without firing a shot.

As the program wound down, I was asked to participate in a new business pursuit. TRW had teamed with Boeing to pursue an anti-satellite program with the Air Force. But they lost in the downselect to two bidders. One survivor, Ling-Temco-Vought, a Dallas aircraft manufacturer, would now compete for the final award. We heard LTV had not received good grades on the software portion of their bids, so TRW decided to pitch our software prowess to them. I was asked to join Jack Distaso in making the presentation. Our Vice President, Bill Besserer, had secured the corporate jet for the trip to Dallas. I loved the convenience of handing my briefcase to the pilot as we boarded the Learjet and took off minutes later from LAX. No waiting. After we landed at Love Field in Dallas we were surprised to be greeted by the LTV President and transported to the plant. Instead of hearing our pitch, the president briefed us on how we could help LTV win the contract. They intended to dump their software teammate, System Development Corporation, and replace them with TRW! We negotiated our teaming agreement and flew back to LA. (I could get used to traveling by private jet.) We arranged for our team, including Jack Dreyfus, Jack Distaso, and me, to help LTV write their "Best and Final" proposal in Dallas. SDC tried to sue LTV for breaking their teaming agreement but were unsuccessful. However, it didn't matter because the LTV/TRW team lost in the final competition.

Another highlight at TRW was my tenth anniversary with the company. I had the honor of having a fascinating dinner with a giant in the aerospace industry, Si Ramo, who founded STL (later, TRW) in 1953. (The "R" stood for Ramo.) His successes were legendary. In 1953, President Eisenhower gave Ramo the contract to develop an ICBM to counter the Soviet threat. Ike said it would be more complex than developing the atomic bomb, which is why he bypassed the contractor giants to award it to STL. Ramo was not only a technology genius (PhDs in physics and electrical engineering at Caltech at age twenty-three), but also an accomplished violinist; he once played a duet with Jascha Heifetz. At age one hundred, he received his final patent, a computer-based learning invention. While I was writing this book, Ramo died at 103.

At the conclusion of our ABM program in 1979, TRW asked me to move my family to Bremen, Germany for the European Space Agency's (ESA) Spacelab Program. Once it became operational, this manned reusable scientific laboratory would be delivered into orbit by the US Shuttle. TRW had an ongoing consulting contract to advise ESA on the development of Spacelab software. But the software development was not going well. The prime contractor, ERNO, headquartered in Bremen, Germany, had to award subcontracts to contractors in twelve countries in proportion to the funding provided by each country. Therefore the prime contractor did not have the financial leverage to keep their subcontractors in line. Four subcontractors in four countries developed the software. The largest was Matra in Paris. ESA wanted TRW to expand our role to manage these software subcontractors. They awarded us a new contract for twelve TRW personnel, six engineers and six managers. TRW wanted me to manage the testing of the software in Bremen. But I knew this would be fraught with problems. We would be testing all of it after the developers completed their work and might not be around to fix the problems we discovered. Instead I wanted to manage the software being developed by Matra in Paris. Obviously this was the coveted assignment, and I lost out to a more experienced TRW manager. It was fortunate that I turned down the Bremen assignment. Bremen's winters and summers sixty miles south of the North Sea were miserable, and my family would not have been happy there. And I was right: the problems found in testing were not easily fixed, requiring extending the tour of duty. Bremen experienced the coldest winter and rainiest summer ever. Not great for a family used to Southern California weather.

24. *Security Clearance—Serious, Not Glamorous*

Many people think a security clearance is glamorous. Just the secrecy and mystery of having access to information which is kept from the general public seems to connote much of the "James Bond, clandestine, cloak and dagger" image. I felt that way before I received my first security clearance.

In June of 1960, at age nineteen, my summer job at the defense division of General Motors required me to have my first clearance. At the time I thought that was pretty cool. The USAF awarded GM a contract to develop and build the guidance system for the Air Force's Titan II Program. Titan II, a new intercontinental ballistic missile launched and delivered nuclear weapons as the primary deterrent to all-out nuclear war with the Soviet Union. Therefore the guidance system had components and documents that received classification by the Department of Defense (DOD) according to the harm their disclosure could bring if they fell into enemy hands. Badges of different colors were issued and prominently worn to designate the highest level of security for which each individual was cleared. The colors for each classification were:

- Grey - Unclassified
- Blue - CONFIDENTIAL
- Red - SECRET
- Red and white - TOP SECRET

As part of the pre-employment paperwork, I had to fill out a security questionnaire detailing my past ten years of addresses, employment, educational institutions, relatives, foreign travel, etc. On my first day, I received my blue badge—CONFIDENTIAL. Later, after the FBI completed a minimal background check, it was upgraded to red, authorizing me access to SECRET information. Again, I thought I was pretty cool. However, one needs both proper authorization and the "need-to-know" before actually obtaining access. I didn't see a SECRET document until the next summer, because only then did I have a need to know the guidance algorithms, the tolerances on the gyroscopes and accelerometers, and the accuracy requirements for the Titan II delivery system in order to do my job. Then I truly learned the downside of a security clearance.

Each SECRET document had to be uniquely numbered, catalogued, and tediously tracked daily by possession. To take it out of the safe, in which it was stored, one needed to memorize the safe's combination and sign out for it in a log. He was then required to prevent unauthorized disclosure every minute it was outside the safe and sign it back in when he returned it. Of course, making copies required elaborate approval and logging processes. At quitting time, a security monitor would verify the safe was properly locked and signed off on the daily log. If a classified document was left out or stored improperly, the person who signed it out would receive a security violation, which was entered into his permanent security record and personnel file. Other violations included leaving the document unattended or the open safe unattended. Two such violations could result in loss of clearance and being fired. A loss of clearance could render a person unemployable in the military field. So the tedious tasks of tracking and logging these documents were important and required discipline.

This became clear at the end of my second summer with GM. One of the engineers in our group had accepted an offer with Honeywell with a nice increase in pay. He turned in his two-week notice and began cleaning out his desk, when security did an inventory on his safe and identified two missing SECRET documents assigned to him. Unable to find them, he had few choices. He could not leave since he would lose his clearance, and Honeywell would not hire him without it. He either had to remain at GM until the documents appeared or until they were downgraded to CONFIDENTIAL (which could take up to 10 years) when a new, advanced system made the Titan's guidance technology obsolete. Of course, there were worse penalties than losing one's clearance. Espionage is charged if a person disclosed classified material on purpose to someone who could pass it on to a foreign government, and the penalties were fines, prison, even death.

But TOP SECRET and SPECIAL ACCESS clearances were much more serious, as I would learn years later.

Although NASA required security clearances for their contractors and employees, they had little need. In my twenty years as a NASA contractor, I never had to sign out a single classified document. I did have access to several SECRET documents when I worked on the Ballistic Missile Defense Program with TRW in California in the late 70's. But when I joined Ultrasystems in 1979, I had to apply for a TOP SECRET DOD clearance as well as a SPECIAL ACCESS clearance or SPECIALLY COMPARTMENTED INFORMATION (SCI) clearance required by the Intelligence Community:

- the Central Intelligence Agency (CIA),
- the Defense Intelligence Agency (DIA),
- the National Security Agency (NSA), and
- the National Reconnaissance Office (NRO) of the USAF.

These required a much longer Personnel Security Questionnaire (PSQ) and an extensive background investigation conducted by the FBI. Some also required a polygraph. From 1982 through 1997, I would be involved with each of these organizations as their contractor, subcontractor, or in pursing new business opportunities with them.

The clearances prohibit me, by law, from disclosing (even to my wife) any details about the work we did. At the time, we were not allowed to even mention the names of these organizations. Even the existence of the NRO was classified at that time. This was referred to as "the black world." Ultrasystems had another line of business—the cogeneration energy construction business—a positive for both the NRO and the NSA since this helped to cover their covert work with these organizations. If we sought a new job, we were not allowed to divulge anything in our résumés and interviews about what we did, beyond broad generics. Reading the classified material and discussions about it could only take place inside the "vault." This is a facility, also called a SCIF (Specially Compartmented Information Facility) with no windows, whose walls were lined with material to inhibit a "listening device" from picking up microwave or electromagnetic signals from the classified computers inside. The phones were specially encrypted and color-coded. They were called "hello" phones because when these phones rang, the answerer was to say "hello," rather than one's name or the name of the company, to further prevent disclosure that the company was doing business with one of the agencies.

The only reasons I am permitted to discuss a small portion of the information at this time is because the existence of the NRO was declassified in 1992, and the technology we used has since been superseded by new evolution. Still, much of the scope of work—the performance of the sensors on the satellites, and even the missions—remain classified in the early 21st century. Most of it will remain classified for many years. I can say only that it involved high-resolution satellite surveillance, commonly referred to as "spy satellites." It was true that without a clearance, one could obtain some information about the programs from several books, technical magazines, and newspaper articles published in the 1970s and '80s, but people with clearances were prohibited from confirming or denying the veracity of these publications.

Obtaining these clearances was quite involved. It could take well over a year, due to the extensive background investigation. The FBI started with the information on the twenty-plus pages of the PSQ. They investigated any relatives living in foreign countries, all overseas travel, and the non-relative references which had to span the last fifteen years with no gaps. Then they asked these people for other references not listed in the PSQ. I remember how surprised and excited my golf pro was when contacted by an FBI agent who asked personal questions about me. (Where did Kurth acquire the money to join a private club? Does he regularly play golf with people traveling to foreign countries? Do you know any reason why he might compromise loyalty to the US Government?)

After all the background investigations and one or more in-depth one-on-one interviews, most agencies required the polygraph as the final step. My first one took place at NSA Headquarters in Fort Mead, Maryland. They wired me up to a machine to measure my blood pressure, perspiration, heartbeat, and nervousness as they asked the preplanned questions. The questions were few, but relevant. They not only asked questions about my loyalty, but also about my lifestyle (e.g. use of drugs, sexual preferences, need for money), since these could be used by a foreign agent as blackmail or leverage to recruit me, particularly if I had something to hide. To ensure that I was not hypnotized or brainwashed in some way to mask the physiological reactions associated with lying, they asked a surprise question. This was intended to register a profound physiological response. My surprise question was mild: "Have you ever lied to your wife?" It really didn't matter whether my answer was "yes" or "no." What mattered was the fact that my graphs showed anxiety. Passing the poly was the final step. After a few weeks I received both my NSA/NRO SPECIAL ACCESS clearance and my DOD TOP SECRET clearance. Then, inside the SCIF, I was "briefed" on the programs and the rules to protect the information from disclosure.

Similarly, I was debriefed when leaving the company, to remind me to maintain silence on the classified information.

I was proud when our son, Scott, received his SPECIAL ACCESS clearance in 1991 to fly the EC-130 aircraft. This had the "Compass Call" equipment in the main cabin. For the first six months, while waiting for his clearance, he had to pilot the plane without being able to enter the main cabin where his crew was performing the SPECIAL ACCESS Compass Call mission. After he was cleared, we were able to talk about his work to a limited extent. I knew about the mission and the equipment because I was in charge of an attempt by Ultrasystems to help Lockheed build the software for the system. Their subcontractor responsible for the software was doing a poor job and they wanted to replace him. Briefly, Compass Call's mission was to perform electronic listening and jamming of enemy communications. However, in the end Lockheed's customer did not want a change, and Lockheed backed down.

The polygraph test is effective in weeding out security risks for people who might have some gripe against the government, need money, or have something to hide. Although it is only 95 percent correct, the errors are almost always on the side of safety. That is, the FBI may occasionally fail someone who is telling the truth, but they will never pass someone who is consciously lying. Around the turn of the 20th to 21st century, they found certain CIA and FBI agents who sold classified information to the Soviet Union/Russia over many years. It is very likely they would have been discovered much earlier, or even been deterred from ever trying it had they been subjected to periodic polygraphs. Both organizations have changed their policies and adopted this practice for all their employees.

At first, it was hard to appreciate the importance of these clearances to my career. But it soon was demonstrated. One of my colleagues at Ultrasystems had come from a related program at TRW, which required a similar clearance, but the CIA sponsored it. As such, they didn't require a polygraph. He flunked his first two NSA polygraphs while at Ultrasystems. When they hooked him up for the third and last try, they asked him his name, and his answer caused the needle to swing off the scale. They unhooked him and asked what his problem was. He unloaded: he was very angry because the poly was intrusive. His demonstration of loyalty on past programs should have been enough evidence for receiving the clearance. After getting it all off his chest, they hooked him up again and he passed the test. But they flunked him anyway for "wrong attitude." The end result was that he had to leave Ultrasystems since he could never be cleared to work on the program. Also, this failure to be cleared would be in his personnel file wherever he worked in the industry, thus limiting his job options.

Another episode of note occurred at TRW back in 1978. A lower level employee, Christopher Boyce, was convicted of selling secrets from the TRW "vault" to the Soviet Union. The story was in all the newspapers, but TRW was prohibited by the agency from commenting on it. (Later the whole story was published as a book, *The Falcon and the Snowman*, and then made into a movie.) George Solomon, TRW's Executive VP and General Manager of Space & Defense, was holding his annual meeting for all the managers. There were over two hundred of us in attendance. He began his business agenda and said he would entertain questions afterward, as usual, but **no one** would be allowed to ask questions about the Boyce incident. Apparently one person was not paying attention, because his first question was regarding the Boyce espionage. I had never seen Solomon (a quiet, even-tempered executive) get so angry and red-faced. He had the individual removed and, I've been told, fired on the spot! TRW was vulnerable to losing one or more of their covert contracts because of the security lapses involved in the Boyce scandal and could not afford to upset the agency with public discussions about it. Solomon made an example of that manager.

In 1980, when Sue and I took our first cruise, the ship docked at a Caribbean island at the same port as a Russian cruise ship. We declined an invitation to board and explore the ship. When I returned to work and mentioned this, I was told I could have been in big trouble had I boarded, since this was Soviet territory, enabling them to legally detain me.

It has been reported that both the US and Soviet Union were guilty of playing spy games in the construction of the embassies in Moscow and Washington DC. For their embassy, the Soviets selected a high-rise building in Washington where they installed microwave eavesdropping equipment in perfect line-of-sight to pick up telephone conversations from several US federal facilities. The US installed a major tunnel under this building so we could eavesdrop on them. The new US embassy in Moscow was built by the Soviets, who honeycombed the building with bugs. Both knew what the other was doing, so it was just a big, expensive game of espionage.

Some of the security clearance rigor had a dramatic change after Bill Clinton took office. I noticed it particularly when I had my last polygraph in 1995. The agents could no longer ask questions about lifestyle. All the questions were restricted to personal espionage intent and past action. I do not know whether this was related in any way to Clinton's own views about lifestyle. The agent administering the test thought it was profoundly related.

I encountered an interesting twist to security measures for TOP SECRET and SPECIAL ACCESS at the USAF Space Command's Combined Space and Operations Center at Colorado Springs. It was the first time I attempted to enter this facility for a meeting. I was ushered to a tiny stand-alone room that looked like a phone booth. When I entered I had to look into a device for a retinal scan. This identified me from a data base that included my retinal signature. I passed this step, but took too long to subsequently enter the security code. Bells rang and lights flashed. I was locked into the "phone booth" until they came to release me. Then I had to go through the same procedure again, but more quickly, before the door opened enabling me to enter the base.

25. *Ultrasystems*

Soon after I turned down the Spacelab assignment in Germany and started looking for my next position with TRW, I was contacted by Phil Stevens. Phil was a former TRW Program Manager and told me I was referred to him by a TRW colleague, but he wouldn't give me his name. He had founded a small private aerospace company ten years earlier, and he wanted to discuss an opportunity with his company in Irvine. I told him I was happy with TRW and was progressing nicely on my career path. But he suggested treating me to a great lunch, and I had nothing to lose hearing him out. Four lunch meetings later, I accepted his offer as an Assistant Vice President with a nice raise and stock options. Since I recognized the risk of joining such a small company, I negotiated a two-month's salary severance package. I was also enticed by the fact my thirty-three-mile commute up the congested 405 Freeway would be reduced to five miles. Ultrasystems was doing revenue of $15 million per year, $14 million with the USAF and Army with some work for a classified customer. Stevens expected to grow by hiring key people who could win military contracts, but he also had a desire to diversify in non-military work.

My new title was flattering, but more for show. My boss, VP Phil Simons, had the total P&L responsibility for the division.

I lead a team to try to win an Air Force contract for independently testing the software for a classified antisatellite system. It was to launch a SRAM-Altair missile from a modified F-15 at 38,000 feet to destroy the targeted satellite with a nuclear warhead. Had we won, it would have doubled the company's revenues. But we lost the close competition to Logicon, who had been marketing the program for years. Although Ultrasystems had a few talented engineers, I began to become disenchanted with the general caliber of technical personnel and started to miss TRW. My proposal staff's shortcomings had forced me to rewrite much of their material.

Stevens then hired Col. John Dean who was retiring as head of a division responsible for USAF highly classified surveillance satellites. Through Dean, Ultrasystems won contracts to support these programs. We built a SCIF, which was essential for all work to protect the highly classified information. All who worked on the projects required clearances that went beyond TOP SECRET, required background checks conducted by the FBI, and passing a polygraph test every five years. Soon after I obtained these clearances, I was briefed on the programs. The classified customer was the NRO. At the time even the existence of the NRO was classified, but no longer. Although we hired more competent engineers, the staff qualifications were still lacking compared to those I knew at TRW. My misgivings with the management and the staff caused me to consider leaving the company. I began to read books on making a job change as a middle manager. At age 42, making $58,000/year, finding an equivalent job might not be as easy as in the past.

Moreover, Stevens used the profits from the military business to expand his diversification goals. He hired a few people who knew something about energy cogeneration, a process for generating electricity and using the byproduct of heat for practical applications instead of discarding it. Phil orchestrated a scenario that Ultrasystems had expertise in this area. He convinced Proctor and Gamble that he could build a cogeneration plant for them. He had me move my engineers to drafting tables when P&G toured our plant, so that it looked like they were designing cogeneration systems. And he acquired a sole-source $20 million project to build it for them. Stevens was a talented salesman. Soon we had multiple cogeneration contracts and that part of the business grew faster than our military business.

When we were approaching a $100 million company, Stevens took Ultrasystems public. Before the Initial Public Offering (IPO) the stock split three-to-one and opened at $12/share. I may have been the only one not excited. I could tell that the company was a house of cards that would eventually fall. I started looking for a new job. I received offers from TRW (thirty-three miles away), Hughes (sixteen miles away), and Intermetrics (five miles away). Just before I left, the stock had split again at five-to-three and was now $25/share. I had sold most of mine but still had a few shares left. Before I was able to sell, it dropped to $19/share, which was still a big profit. In a few years, the house of cards collapsed. The stock had dropped to $2/share before Ultrasystems was bought out at $4/share.

I accomplished one more victory just days before I left Ultrasystems. I personally wrote a winning proposal to IBM Federal Systems Division for a small subcontract to support the ground control software for the Defense Support Program. This exposed me, for the first time, to the two DSP missions: early warning of missile launches and earth surveillance. Although I would not be working on this new Ultrasystems subcontract, this cursory knowledge would become valuable to me ten years later.

26. *The Business Side of Aerospace–Not Dull*

At first glance the aerospace industry seems like most others. The customer wants an excellent job performance at a minimal price. The contractor wants to satisfy the customer while maximizing his profit. It would be similar to our selecting a contractor to build a room addition to our home. Both the contractor and we want the job done right with high quality and on-time performance. The conflict arises in the price. We are at the mercy of the contractor who is much more knowledgeable about the details of the job and the materials. If we agree to a cost-plus-fee contract, we are worried he will run up the costs to ensure the quality, since he has no immediate fee incentive to do otherwise. If we agree to a firm-fixed-price contract, he is able to charge us extra (likely enhancing his profit) for any change to the original agreement on the specifications.

How do we know if the price is fair and his profit is not exorbitant? To solve this conflict, we use the free-enterprise tool of competition. We do our best in generating specifications for the addition and send it out for competitive bids. Assuming there are several contractors interested in our job, competitive pricing will protect us from being gouged. We enter into a contract with the winning bidder which includes the specifications and the terms and conditions, such as schedule, fee, and price.

Ostensibly, government agencies try to do the same. But the process is fraught with potential problems, due to two principal causes:

1) The government agency is working with taxpayers' money

2) The US Congress defines the buying process to protect the government against contractor and buyer improprieties, incompetence, and performance deficiencies with virtually no regard for the cost of these protections.

The Congress has developed a set of Federal Acquisition Regulations that document in boring, expensive detail exactly how they are to acquire goods and services. This has driven the cost of ordinary purchases for government to outrageous proportions such as the "$600 toilet seat" and "$100 hammer" reported in the media.

While progressing up the management ladder, I recognized my deficiencies in business acumen. So I took advantage of every opportunity to master the business side of the industry. TRW invited me to take the Vince Lombardi course on management training, emphasizing motivation. I learned how to write compelling business proposals from seminars by experienced professionals. TRW sent me to a class on generating hard-hitting Power-Point presentations using assertive titles for each slide, proving each one with the underlying material.

While at Intermetrics I spent a week at the UCLA Graduate School of Management learning the Japanese techniques of Total Quality Management. I applied them to improve our administrative functions. I devoured an intensive two-week course at the Stanford Executive Institute, touted as a mini MBA. I joined the Southern California Technology Executive Network (SO/CAL/TEN). This round-table of a dozen CEOs and General Managers met four hours every month to help each other with their business problems. SO/CAL/TEN also sponsored several speakers each year including UCLA basketball coach John Wooden, NFL quarterback Fran Tarkenton, and several founders and CEOs of successful Silicon Valley high-tech firms. A three-day course on risk management at Aerojet taught me that government and its contractors were too risk-averse, which inhibited effective decision making.

27. *Intermetrics*

I accepted the offer with Intermetrics (a spin-off of Draper Labs) in 1983 in Huntington Beach. Intermetrics, a small $50 million company headquartered in Cambridge Massachusetts, had gone public less than two years prior. I was acquainted with four of the five founders: Ed Copps, Jim Miller, Dan Likely, and John Miller, from my work at the Lab sixteen years earlier. John was CEO and Chairman of the Board of Directors. I had interviewed with Copps and his boss, Joe Saponaro, VP and General Manager of the Aerospace Systems Group (ASG). I told Joe that I aspired to become a GM in the aerospace industry. This was perfect because he expected to replace John Miller as President, and he would be looking for his own replacement for the GM slot. I also knew Joe from the Lab. He led a small team of people from System Development Corporation in 1967, hired to support the integration and put the final touches on the Apollo software before deployment. So he was familiar with my work there.

My offer at Intermetrics only matched the same salary I had at Ultrasystems because I had just received a good raise the previous month, just after I interviewed with Joe. It was also lower than the other two offers I had received from TRW and Hughes. But I felt certain this was the best long term opportunity for me. I would be just another senior engineer or middle manager at the much larger companies of TRW or Hughes. (And I would have to resume the long commute in LA traffic.) ASG was doing $8 million/year in revenues. They had won a GPS contract with the Air Force to test the terminal receivers for the military. Their other contracts were with NASA and Rockwell involving Shuttle software. Saponaro's domain had grown from a ten-person office to almost one hundred people in a few years, identifying him as a rising star in the company. ASG now had small offices in Houston, Texas, Seattle, Washington, and Huntsville,

Alabama—in addition to the ASG headquarters in Huntington Beach, California.

My initial title, Director of New Business Development, was indicative of the primary growth objective for this small, now public, company. At its Cambridge headquarters, Intermetrics had developed a technology lead in a software language, Ada, which the US Department of Defense chose as a standard for all military software development. Ada (named after one of the first female programmers) was a state-of-the art, powerful, object-oriented, high order language facilitating the development and maintenance of military software. Intermetrics had helped to design the language, and the Cambridge group won several contracts to develop Ada compilers.[3] I recognized this technology edge as a discriminator in competing for military software contracts. I also believed we could capitalize on our GPS contract to compete for other government contracts to test new software systems, a process known as Independent Verification and Validation (IV&V). So I quickly learned as much as I needed about Intermetrics qualifications in those two areas in order to sell the customers on our expertise prior to bidding (writing proposals) for related competitions. I also brought in a consultant to teach our engineers how to write winning proposals.

I made presentations to various program offices at the USAF Space and Missile Division in El Segundo. Although I received a warm reception from various USAF Colonels, I decided to bid on only one opportunity there, which we lost. I could surmise that Logicon had all the IV&V competitions wired. They were a larger organization that had built their reputation on military IV&V. Their customers wanted us to compete with them, but to get Logicon's price down, not because they wanted a different contractor.

---

[3] A compiler translates the easily-understood programmer source code into machine language code directly understood by the computer.

I did compete for four small contracts with a different division of the USAF at Wright-Patterson AFB to develop Ada software tools. We won all four. Our Cambridge counterparts also won a contract with the same organization to develop an Ada compiler. But we decided to use an existing operational Ada compiler not built by Intermetrics in order to reduce the risk. As a result, our four contracts were highly successful, while the Cambridge compiler was a disaster. Had we proceeded to wait for the Cambridge compiler, our contracts would not have succeeded. So, just as Saponaro left for Cambridge to become President, my reputation with top management rose, and I was promoted to General Manager. John Miller retained the position of Chairman of the Board.

One of my first assignments as GM was to close our five-person Huntsville office, which was losing money. They had only one contract: building a Spacelab experiment simulator. Spacelab was a scientific laboratory under development by the European Space Agency to be carried onboard the Shuttle. But I didn't want to give up the office without a fight. I flew to Huntsville and met with NASA's Marshall Space Flight Center management. Marshall's Director and famous space visionary, Wernher von Braun, had retired after developing the highly successful Saturn rockets. I gave a presentation to several Marshall managers, showing how we would be forced to close our local office unless we could count on enough business to sustain us: $500,000 per year. I was amazed when my challenge was accepted. They thought enough of our Spacelab test support subsystem to determine whether they could find enough business to sustain us. Months later they concluded they could not meet our needs. So I began to close the office. I set up four goals in doing so:

1. Don't lose more money in the process.
2. Leave the Marshall management with positive feelings about Intermetrics.
3. Transfer the five employees to Huntington Beach.

4. Maintain our Spacelab experiment simulator so it could be utilized for the Shuttle.

We achieved three of the four goals. We sold the rights to the Spacelab simulator to another contractor for $110,000. But our local employees refused to leave Huntsville and were hired by local companies.

On one of my last trips to Huntsville, I had time to peruse the Visitor Center. Marshall has a great museum of their past rockets and accomplishments. But I was shocked to find several errors in their display of planetary phenomenon. I actually wrote down six factual errors. I gave these to the Assistant Curator, who seemed offended by my findings. Then I listened to a young docent, standing in front of a mockup of the Apollo LM, telling how it descended to the moon. She said the engine was shut off, allowing the LM to **fall** the last 500 feet! After her presentation, I took her aside and explained that the astronauts took control of the LM's computer at 500 feet to avoid any uneven landing spot, but were to nominally descend at three feet per second. Then I pointed to the

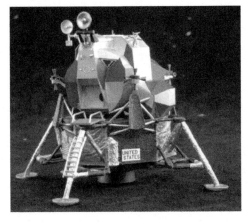

11-inch probes attached to the landing pods and told her that when they touched the surface, only then would the engine shut down allowing the LM to fall less than one foot! If it fell from a higher altitude, the engine bell could bottom out causing an explosion. I suggested that both she and the Curator contact Marshall's engineers who could verify what I told them.

Then it was back to California to grow ASG. Saponaro had been convinced that our business would continue to grow. He had just signed a ten-year lease for the 25,000 square feet we currently occupied in Huntington Beach, plus another 8,000-square-foot annex. Maybe he didn't foresee the feast and famine roller coaster in the NASA and DOD funding that I saw. My problem now was that our facility space was almost twice our needs, driving our overhead costs higher than our competitors. Nevertheless we did grow the ASG business to $19 million and 180 employees at its peak in 1990, mostly in the Seattle and Houston offices. We expanded our solid staff of engineers and software developers. Their high level of performance was critical to our success. We won the re-competition of our GPS IV&V contract, and after the *Challenger* tragedy we won a $20 million contract to certify the Shuttle flight software for each mission. But we eventually lost two giant opportunities. ...

28. *The Space Shuttle—Operational Phase*

The maiden manned Shuttle test was STS-1[4] launched 12 April 1981, exactly twenty years since man first entered space. Its only crew

consisted of Commander John Young and Pilot Bob Crippen. This was the first American manned mission since Apollo/Soyuz in 1975.

They were in orbit fifty-four hours, traversing thirty-seven revolutions around the earth at an altitude of 167 miles, before returning to a successful landing in the *Columbia* orbiter. Our neighbor, Dick Truly was the backup pilot. He later flew the Shuttle and reached the level of Vice Admiral before becoming the first astronaut appointed NASA Administrator in 1989.

---

[4] The STS designation stood for Shuttle Transportation System.

When I joined Intermetrics in 1983 I became intimately involved in Shuttle again. Half of our $8 million in revenues were with Shuttle contacts and subcontracts. When I took over as General Manager more than half of my one hundred employees were working on the program. My Houston office was maintaining the HAL compiler, a software program written by Intermetrics and used by NASA, IBM, and Rockwell to write and maintain the Shuttle flight software. Shuttle had a requirement to be fail-operational, fail-safe. That is, incorporating redundancy, it was to continue the operational mission after one failure, but to abort and return safely after a second failure. To meet these requirements, four copies of this avionics software were loaded into four identical flight computers to provide triple redundancy. The avionics commands from the four computers were compared before issuing. If they were not identical, the one anomalous command would mean its computer was faulty and it would be taken offline. We were also under contract to Rockwell International, the Shuttle prime contractor, to create the flight loads for a fifth avionics computer. Rockwell developed this software by using our compiler to create an independent backup, just in case there was a flaw in IBM's primary flight software. It could be detected by comparisons, and then the backup system would take over the flight.

In Houston we also helped JSC plan the Shuttle missions. At the Marshall Space Center in Huntsville we supported NASA in using the experiment simulator we had developed for the International Spacelab payload to be flown on future Shuttle Missions. John Hanaway had retired from NASA and now managed my Seattle office, which had a small study contract with NASA.

On 16 November 1982, before I joined Intermetrics, I took our family to watch the *Columbia* orbiter land at Edwards AFB[5] in the California

---

[5] Edwards was a backup landing site to be used if the primary site at Cape Canaveral had weather problems.

high desert. This was the fifth Shuttle mission and the first operational mission, all with *Columbia*. Although it had only a crew of four, this was the largest crew in an American spacecraft at that time. The STS-5 mission successfully delivered the first two commercial satellites into low earth orbit, which were then boosted with their own propulsion systems to their final geosynchronous orbits at 23,000 miles, such that they would rotate over a fixed point above the earth's equator and appear stationary from the earth. *Columbia* had traveled over two million miles in 81 orbits over five days.

We got up well before dawn to drive the two hours to Edwards, get our car pass, and wait for the 6:33 AM landing. It was amazing. This was no ordinary glider. The landing sequence started on the opposite side of the world. The RCS thrusters fired to reorient the orbiter backward to the 17,000 mph velocity, and the Orbital Maneuvering System (OMS) thrusters fired to reduce the speed by 200 mph. (The three main engines that completed the boost to orbit are now not functional since the external tank that provided fuel was jettisoned during boost.) This enabled the orbiter to reach the upper atmosphere twenty-five minutes later. The onboard computers then reoriented it back to flying forward and pitched the bottom forty degrees toward the atmosphere. As it entered the atmosphere the friction heated up *Columbia* to 3000°F, and the ionized air inhibited ground communication for twelve minutes. After the computers executed a series of S-shaped turns to further reduce the speed and begin its final approach to the runway, the crew took control. We first heard the double sonic boom as *Columbia* began its final approach to the Edwards runway, specially built long enough to accommodate the orbiter landing. Then we saw this dot appear out of the sky. In a matter of seconds it was large enough to see the shape of the orbiter. A few seconds later it was touching the ground. It was a glider that flew like a rock! I was not prepared for how fast this space vehicle descended from barely visible to touchdown. The 122-foot, 152,000-

pound orbiter, with a 78-foot wingspan, has no propulsive engines for landing. It had to glide to touchdown. And with no engines, there is no such thing as aborting the landing and turning around for another pass. I think my kids were as impressed as Sue and I were. Once the rear wheels were on solid ground, the parachutes opened to aid the braking. It still traveled a  long way on the runway before the nose wheels touched ground and eventually came to a stop. I almost expected to feel the heat from the reentry shield tiles as the orbiter passed by. It was exciting.

In January 1986 I arrived at my office in Huntington Beach in time to watch Shuttle Launch, STS-51-L, on TV in our conference room. (The STS numbering system was complex—an attempt to indicate fiscal year, launch site, and sequence.) Viewing the launch was a usual practice at all three of my offices. It always gave the employees a lift to see the fruits of their labor playing a part in each successful Shuttle mission. There were perhaps twenty of us gathered around the TV. The launch had been delayed a bit due to the unusually cold weather at the cape. The cameras actually showed icicles hanging from the vehicle earlier in the morning. The mission was to deliver the first USAF Tracking and Data Relay Satellite to orbit.

There had been several delays lately, and NASA's launch schedule had been cut back. This was only the tenth flight of the *Challenger* orbiter, and NASA was under fire for not meeting their goal of at least twelve flights per year. This, together with the cost overruns, caused the cost per flight to far exceed the goal of a ten-fold reduction in the payload-to-orbit costs promised at the program outset. To compensate for this public relations problem, NASA had begun sending civilians onboard. Two congressmen had flown in the Shuttle in the past year. Now, on this flight, Christa McAuliffe, a young schoolteacher, was part of the seven-person crew.

The final countdown had begun and was proceeding smoothly. The liftoff was nominal, and we all expressed signs of relief and joy when the Shuttle cleared the tower and soared upward. The TV cameras zoomed in on the rapidly accelerating vehicle as the solid rocket motors proceeded to burn. Then suddenly it appeared that the Shuttle exploded! We all watched in horror and disbelief as the solid rocket motors (SRMs) appeared to blow away from what was left of the external tank and the orbiter and continued to burn off at angles from

the explosion, forming grotesque plumes of smoke in the sky. No one could survive that blast! (Later it was discovered that some of the crew may have survived prior to hitting the water at a fatal speed.) What could have caused such a disaster after  twenty-four successful flights? NASA commissioned an independent panel of experts to dig into the problem, find the answers, and make recommendations on how to prevent any such occurrence in the future. We were sure our work on the compilers and flight software had nothing to do with the tragedy, but we were included in the investigation. The cause turned out to be the cold weather freezing an

O-ring that formed a seal between the section joints of the solid rocket motor system, resulting in a seal failure, burning through the SRM, ultimately separating both SRMs from the external fuel tank, which began breaking up in the atmosphere, creating a fireball.

One of the distinguished members of the *Challenger* Investigation Commission was Dr. Richard Feynman, a famous theoretical physicist who had worked on the Manhattan Project early in his career. He received the Nobel Prize for his work in physics. As one of the measures to reduce risk to future Shuttle flights, he recommended that NASA hire a qualified contractor to perform an independent verification of the IBM-developed Shuttle flight software prior to each mission.

In 1975, when Shuttle development was just beginning, I had made the same recommendation for TRW to perform this function for the Shuttle Program. I had convinced Dr. Ken Cox, Director of the Avionics Division that software was a vulnerable risk to flight safety. Virtually every other subsystem was doubly or triply redundant and could withstand at least one failure. But an error in the guidance, navigation, or control software had no redundancy since the same software was in each of the four primary flight computers, and therefore could cause a catastrophic failure. Cox became our NASA sponsor and took the proposal to Chris Kraft, Director of JSC. But Kraft didn't like the idea. He set up some difficult criteria:

- All the NASA technical experts involved must agree that independent verification and validation (IV&V) would work.
- IV&V must be shown to be the most cost effective technical solution to the software safety problem.
- The funding would have to come from a source other than Kraft's budget.

We met all three criteria, including persuading Aaron Cohen, Shuttle Program Manager, to provide the funding. Nevertheless Kraft turned us down. Neither we nor Cox understood why.

Years later, after I had left TRW in Houston, it was decided that Rockwell would develop an independent version of the critical phases of the guidance and control software, load it into a fifth computer, and switch to it in real time in the event of a failure of the primary flight software developed by IBM. Intermetrics ultimately received a subcontract from Rockwell to help with the development of the "backup" flight software, which we were doing at the time of the *Challenger* disaster.

The *Challenger* disaster brought the Shuttle Program to a halt. No new missions would be flown until all problems were fixed and the safety was improved. I was concerned that as much as 50 percent of my Intermetrics business would be put on hold for more than a year. But the Feynman recommendation could save us. Next to Rockwell and IBM, only we were technically qualified to perform an IV&V of the flight software. But IBM and Rockwell couldn't do it because they were not independent. TRW had long since lost their intimate knowledge of the avionics system and software. We were not totally "independent" because of our work with the compilers and the backup system. But no one else could begin to learn the details of 200,000 lines of HAL code in the primary computers in time to validate the software for each mission.

The Feynman recommendation met some resistance at NASA. But within months we received a sole source contract to perform IV&V for the next mission. We helped Bob Moorehead from NASA's Shuttle Program Office write a perfect sole source justification for us to perform the job. At Moorehead's request, I assigned John Hanaway, Director of my Seattle Division, to lead the effort with the work divided between my Seattle and Houston offices. (John had been one of the designers of the Shuttle Avionics System when he was Director of the JSC Avionics Division before he came to Intermetrics.) I left my Huntington Beach office out of it since they had the subcontract with Rockwell for the Backup System, and therefore could not be viewed as "independent." The contract saved us. We began work with abandon and were ready to formally certify the next flight a year later. We continued to perform this role for each subsequent Shuttle mission, giving Intermetrics national visibility throughout the Shuttle community. Ultimately we had to compete for the follow-on contract for all future flights. We easily won this contract in 1991, worth a minimum of $20 million in revenues for Intermetrics.

But we had another hurdle to overcome in 1988, soon after Feynman's death. I suddenly received a summons for all my Shuttle records from a federal prosecutor in Houston. This included boxes and boxes of documentation, emails, and even my personal Day-Timer calendar from 1986 to the present. I was also ordered to appear before a federal grand jury in Houston. The prosecutor alleged that Bob Moorehead, now the newly appointed NASA Program Manager for Space Station, had committed an impropriety in awarding Intermetrics the sole-source contract. The only thing that could cause suspicion along this line of thinking was that Bob's wife, Delores, worked in my Houston office as one of our senior program managers. But I made sure she was never involved in any contract in which Bob played any role. Nevertheless, the prosecutor apparently thought he could find something in his witch hunt. When I finally received the summons to testify in front of this grand jury, the prosecutor had studied all my records—those from my Houston and Seattle offices, and my CEO's records—for months. Joe Saponaro, John Hanaway, and my Houston Director (Delores Moorehead's boss) were also called to testify. After asking me fewer than ten questions, the prosecutor was finished and asked me if I had anything else I wanted to say. I told the grand jury that this whole thing had no merit, was a waste of time for Intermetrics, and was unnecessarily costing our small company time and money. Two weeks later, we received our documents back and never heard anything more about the matter.

In March of 1989, a few months after STS returned to operational status, Aaron Cohen—now the Director of JSC—sent me a formal invitation as one of the VIPs to see the launch of the orbiter *Discovery*. I was happy to accept. I was proud to be there with other executives from the aerospace industry whose companies had contributed to the Shuttle Program. I had not personally witnessed a live launch of any kind since Apollo 16 in April 1972. The STS-29[6] mission was to deliver the Tracking and Data Relay Satellite into orbit, as well as eight experiment payloads. I flew to Orlando the day before the launch, and drove to Coco Beach where I spent the night. It brought back wonderful memories of the Apollo glamour days, including the liftoff parties in Coco Beach.

The National Aeronautics and Space Administration cordially invites you to attend a **Launch of the Space Shuttle** at the John F. Kennedy Space Center, Florida

R.S.V.P. *As soon as possible.*

My car pass allowed me to drive around the Kennedy Space Center the next morning, which also brought back great memories of this historic place. An hour before the scheduled launch, I arrived at the viewing stands, across the Banana River 3.5 miles from the launch pad. As a VIP, I sat in the bleachers just in front of the enormous

---

[6] The STS numbering system was changed back after *Challenger*.

Vehicle Assembly Building that housed the Shuttle prelaunch stacks. This was the same building in which all the Apollo/Saturn stacks had been assembled two decades earlier. But compared to my memories of the 363-feet high Apollo/Saturn stack, the Shuttle looked quite small at just over one hundred feet high. It was impressive, however, with the Orbiter strapped to the large orange external tank and the two solid rocket motors fastened to the sides. It was a beautiful, warm, sunny day with very few clouds to interfere with our view of the launch. Although the dignitaries seemed excited in anticipation of the launch, for me it could not compare to the excitement of the Saturn launches a decade earlier.

The countdown from the bunkered control room near the launch pad was broadcast to the VIP area. As the count entered the last minute, we held our breath, worried about a possible malfunction that might stop the launch or worse— especially after the tragic *Challenger* disaster. But the count continued as programmed, the solids ignited, and ... it was gone! The Shuttle cleared the launch tower so fast; it was well on its way by the time we heard the roar of the solid rocket motors, the sound taking more than fifteen

170

seconds to reach us. It was so different from the Saturn. The solid rocket motors built to maximum thrust in one-tenth of a second—far unlike the eight seconds it took for the five Saturn engines to build to 90 percent maximum thrust, while being held in place by the rocker arms at the bottom of the launch pad. The initial thrust of the solids was 1.6 times the pull of gravity, compared to Saturn's 1.1, resulting in the dramatic change in how fast it cleared the tower. Similarly, the Shuttle disappeared quickly as it soared through the atmosphere, seeking orbital velocity of 17,700 miles per hour. The show ended much too quickly. But it was majestic nevertheless. I felt a similar national pride as I enjoyed the launch, but not nearly as much as the Apollo launches. Still, I had a feeling of satisfaction as I drove back to Orlando for my flight home.

29. GPS—Much More Than Military

My first introduction to the Global Positioning System came in 1979, soon after leaving TRW to join Ultrasystems. We needed some new business opportunities, and the Air Force Space and Missile Systems Command in El Segundo was holding a conference on upcoming bidding opportunities for contractors. The USAF GPS Program Office spent  four hours telling us about this new program to provide a revolutionary worldwide navigation system for the entire military. The major development contracts for the Space Segment, the Control Segment, and the User Segment were in the final stages of source selection. The military, like NASA, usually downselects to two or three finalist contractors for the design and development of the major segments of the system. Then, they compete for the first multibillion dollar production phase. The conference was to identify other, smaller bidding opportunities for small businesses planned for the near future.

Originally, the Space Segment consisted of twenty-four operational satellites (plus on-orbit spares), four in each of six orbital planes inclined at fifty-five degrees to the equator, circling the earth at 12,600 miles altitude, once

every twelve hours. This orbital architecture would allow for five to eight satellites being visible from any spot on earth at any time. Today there are an additional seven satellites to improve accuracy to every location on earth. Each satellite continuously transmits its precisely known position and time signal, based on an atomic clock onboard.

The User Segment consists of terminals each with an antenna to receive the precision-timed signals from the satellites in view. These data are fed to a self-contained computer, which, through a series of complex calculations based on triangulation, computes the latitude, longitude and altitude of the terminal. Although theoretically three satellite signals would suffice to compute the location, the redundant extra signals from the other visible satellites are necessary to sync the time and greatly increase the accuracy of the terminal position.

The Control Segment is a typical ground station for command and control of the satellites. It issues commands to the propulsion jets on the satellites to accurately position them in orbit after deployment by the rocket booster; it monitors their health, and controls their positions and attitude for station-keeping. It also switches out any defective or dead satellites with available on-orbit spares.

The Program is fascinating and its potential applications, enormous. Once the full constellation of satellites was in place, anyone with only a small, smart receiver (terminal) and no other aids would know exactly where he was anywhere on dry ground, water, or in the air (below the satellite altitude) within twenty feet (assuming unobstructed line-of-sight to the satellites and negligible atmospheric disturbance). And if he had two receivers a few hundred feet apart and one receiver's position was well known (as a fixed landmark on dry ground), the other's position could be determined within an error of inches! This application, known as Differential GPS, uses the known relative location to calibrate the error. This would allow, for example, a person to measure the amount of flex in Hoover Dam. The first and best-known military application came in the Desert Storm War in Iraq and Kuwait in 1991. There were not enough military terminals ready for every foot soldier, so many of their mothers bought commercial GPS receivers and sent them to their sons in case they became separated from their units. However, the Air Force had designed into the system an error source called "Selective Availability." It purposely introduced a slight error into the precision timing signal from the satellites such that the navigation error would increase tenfold. Thus the military could ensure that the enemy's use of the signals would be significantly degraded compared to use by US military receivers. The future debate looming was: should the military be forced to inhibit selective availability so that myriad civilian applications could benefit to the maximum extent possible? In the year 2000 President Clinton directed that Selective Availability be discontinued. All commercial aircraft can now have a GPS receiver onboard, not only for precision navigation, but also for collision avoidance without the help of air traffic controllers, and even for instrument landing.

Although I concluded that Ultrasystems could not successfully compete for any of the upcoming GPS bidding opportunities, I was fascinated with the program and its obvious applications for military and civilian use alike.

Five years earlier, while I was still at TRW and not yet aware of Intermetrics, I had my first, but brief exposure to the GPS Program that would follow me during much of my career (and the rest of my life). Before I left TRW in the spring of 1979, I had lunch with Joe Saponaro. Another Intermetrics VP, Brad Parkinson, was partially credited with inventing GPS when he headed the USAF Program Office as a Colonel before retiring. Joe was gloating! He had just won the contract to perform an Independent Verification and Validation of the GPS User Segment. And this two-hundred-person company had beaten giant TRW in this competition worth over $1,000,000 per year for several years. The irony was that TRW and Intermetrics had planned to team together to win this competition against several other strong competitors, but had parted ways just before the USAF Request for Proposal had been released. Intermetrics insisted on at least $1,000,000 of revenue over the first five years of the contract. TRW's greed clouded their judgment, and they refused Intermetrics' demand. So each company competed separately for the award, resulting in the Intermetrics win. I was not personally involved in the TRW decision or competition, and I was leaning toward leaving TRW for Ultrasystems. So I had no reservations in giving Joe my sincere congratulations in beating TRW, and wished him success in fulfilling the terms of the contract. Little did I know at the time that this win by Intermetrics would have a profound effect on my career.

After I was hired at Intermetrics, the GPS business continued to flourish. We helped the Program Office select the ultimate builders of the military receivers. In addition, we evaluated the performance of many commercial GPS receivers being produced in response to the civilian demand as the satellites became operational. And the commercial applications grew dramatically. We also won the recompetition of our GPS contract to replace the one ending after five years.

Steve Gilbert, a USAF Colonel, had been Brad Parkinson's Deputy in the GPS Program Office prior to retiring and joining Intermetrics' corporate office in Massachusetts. I transferred him to run my California Division in Huntington Beach. Steve led our win of a GPS support contract for the 69th Test Group at Holloman AFB in New Mexico to help the USAF test and evaluate new systems containing the embedded GPS receivers. This required opening a new office in Alamogordo, NM. The Air Force unit invited me, as the lead contractor executive, to cut the ribbon, opening their new navigation test center at Holloman.

GPS was a large part of my Aerospace Systems Group's growth to 180 employees and $19 million in revenues, and it was a major component of my net profit margins of 10 to 15 percent. But

Saponaro declined to allow us to invest any of our profits in our ideas to exploit the commercial end of new applications. Our last idea was to mount receivers in police and emergency helicopters to improve their search for specific ground locations and addresses, replacing their crude, hard-copy maps with digital screens and images. When Saponaro turned down our request for $200,000 to complete the development of prototypes to sell to police, fire, and medical customers, we gave up chasing the GPS commercial applications. In hindsight this was a mistake.

Meanwhile dozens of companies, such as Trimble, Garmin, and Magellan, were born to manufacture smaller, cheaper, lightweight, less ruggedized versions of the receivers. The civilian demand fueled the rapid growth of receiver terminals to annual sales of billions of dollars. Receiver manufacturers began incorporating digital maps targeted to specific applications, making it easier for the civilian user. Small boat owners and giant cruise and tanker ships alike were incorporating these terminals into their navigation systems. The large ships were saving major amounts of fuel by now navigating in straight lines on a great circle arc over the oceans, rather than the more crude zigzag paths that wasted fuel. The smaller pleasure craft and fishing boats were saving lives in storms by knowing exactly where to steer their boats to safety. Aircraft started installing and integrating GPS receivers with their existing navigation systems, but were waiting for the "selective availability" issue to be settled so the FAA would approve GPS as the primary navigation system. It was beginning to be used for large-scale inventory location and control, for mapping and marking the location of road signs and other assets such as trees in a forest and, of course, for vehicle navigation.

Today it is a tool I use almost every day. When I bought my 2001 Lexus GS 300 in November 2000, I opted for the integrated GPS navigation system. This illustrates how far the technology has evolved today. All the roads and cities in the US are digitally mapped on a single DVD. In addition, it contains all the restaurants, gas stations, civic centers, shopping centers, entertainment complexes, hospitals, emergency rooms, golf courses, stadiums, etc. and their addresses and phone numbers. The particular locations are selectively displayed on the map on the screen in the dashboard as the user identifies the point of interest. The car's location—known by the triangulation of the GPS satellite signals picked up by the embedded antenna/receiver—is always displayed on the map. Upon selecting one of these pre-programmed venues or a manually entered location (address, intersection, freeway on-ramp, etc.) as a desired destination, the system determines the entire route—be it around the corner or across the country—according to whether one selects the shortest or fastest route. One can also select a route that avoids freeways, toll roads, and/or auto ferries. As one begins his journey, a voice warns in advance when the next turn is coming, taking the optimal route, turn-by-turn, until the voice says "you have arrived at your destination." This has saved me countless frustrations in trying to find my way to a particular location or venue. I will never get lost. And I love the fact that the voice doesn't scold you when you make the wrong turn. It simply reroutes you from your new present location to your destination or says "make a legal U-turn." The GPS in my 2008 Lexus LS has obvious improvements: updated surface street maps, additional destination options, and voice control for inputting addresses. This stuff is cool!

Sue owns a handheld Magellan GPS terminal, which we use in rental cars when we travel. Her smart phone has similar capabilities. It saves us a lot of stress in different locales. She also owns a wristband Garmin GPS terminal with all the golf courses in the US and Canada programmed into the database. It tells her the distance to the front, center, and back of each green from her current location, although sometimes it is off by over five yards if the receiver is only picking up five satellites.

30. *Sy Rubenstein*

I was introduced to Seymour Rubenstein by Joe Saponaro right after my promotion to General Manager of ASG in the summer of 1984. Sy was president of Rockwell's Space Division in Downey and one of my key customers. Rockwell was the prime contractor for the development and operations of the Space Shuttle Orbiter. For several years we had been creating and testing the flight software loads for the Shuttle backup flight computer for each Shuttle Mission. Rockwell designed and maintained this software. IBM's Federal Systems Division was responsible for the software for the four primary Shuttle Flight Computers.

I was impressed by Sy. I knew of his reputation with the Shuttle Program. He had worked his way up through the Rockwell ranks as Director of System Engineering, Chief Engineer, and Shuttle Program Manager before being promoted to President of the prestigious Space Division. He was credited with solving the Shuttle's start-up problems, especially the faulty adherence of the critical reentry heat-dissipating tiles to the skin of the orbiter. This was one intelligent man—a tireless worker, and a respected executive and leader. Although we had some significant disagreements (like an ant disagreeing with an elephant), they were never personal because we understood that our individual positions were in the best interests of our respective companies.

After Saponaro left California to assume the Intermetrics CEO position in Cambridge Massachusetts, I began to get better acquainted with Rubenstein via occasional one-on-one meetings with him in his impressive office in Downey. It was fun being invited to park in the No-Parking Zone in the circular driveway adjacent to his office. When I met with any of his subordinates, even his VPs, I had to park in the vast Rockwell parking lot and walk several hundred yards to get to the buildings. Sy was easy to talk with about common problems, challenges, and new business, but in the early days these were mostly courtesy visits. I was always fascinated with his insight and how his mind worked. This particularly stood out during our planning meetings in pursuing contracts for the next multibillion-dollar manned spaceflight program, the International Space Station in the late 1980s.

Sy had invited us to join his ISS team, which comprised some of the powerhouse contractors of the industry: Grumman, Harris Corporation, Sperry, TRW, and United Technologies. These were all billion-dollar companies; and here we were, tiny Intermetrics, with revenues of less than $50 million, on an equal level as a Rockwell teammate, to be responsible for developing all the Space Station flight software. Sy selected us based on our successful work on Shuttle flight software and our reputation with NASA. I loved it. Sy would hold periodic strategy meetings with the executive management of these teammates, which I always attended, enabling me to build relationships with them. It was clear to all, however, that Sy was the leader—we the followers. He earned our respect. Among his many awards was the NASA Public Service Medal.

Our counterpart on the competing McDonnell Douglas team was giant IBM, who was not Rockwell's favorite. IBM had convinced NASA to contract directly with them for the Shuttle flight software, rather than be a subcontractor to Rockwell. Since the flight software was an integral part of the critical orbiter avionics system developed by Rockwell, a natural adversarial relationship developed. NASA was happy with this relationship because it kept them in control and exposed avionics and software issues immediately. However, it made resolution of these issues more difficult with NASA having to adjudicate them, rather than the single prime contractor being responsible for their resolution.

Tiny Intermetrics, on the other hand, had been a direct contractor to NASA for the Shuttle support software, such as the design of the HAL software language and the development and maintenance of the HAL compiler used by IBM and Rockwell to build the flight software. In addition, we had small subcontracts with IBM as well as Rockwell.

In the early definition phase of the Space Station, it was not 100 percent clear how NASA would contract for the vast software requirements, both flight and ground. IBM continued to lobby for a separate contract direct to NASA, while Rockwell tried to convince them to make it the responsibility of the prime contractor to enable clear total system responsibility and accountability. Meanwhile, we hedged our bets. Although our role would be much larger if Rockwell were successful, we knew the IBM approach had NASA's favor. By the time NASA announced that the flight software contract would be a separate competition, we had already competed and won a major subcontract role on the IBM team for this upcoming prize. As a result, Rubenstein decided to compete for the flight software with IBM directly; Lockheed was a third competitor. We believed that IBM, with our help, would easily win this competition. If so, this would develop into the largest contract ever for Intermetrics and last for decades! I had even negotiated with IBM to give us part of their existing Shuttle software business if we won. This would allow us to spread our fixed costs across the much larger contractual base, lowering our overhead and administrative rates for the Space Station.

But Sy was incensed. After unsuccessfully trying to convince me and then intimidate me into dumping IBM to join his software bid, he tried to do the same with Saponaro. But Joe backed my play. He was as convinced as I that IBM would win the software competition. Sy threatened to kick us off the prime Space Station team but, instead, just banned us from the strategy sessions to ensure nothing would be leaked to the enemy. He also removed our Intermetrics logo from the marketing and advertising materials being produced for the prime competition. Our personnel working at Rockwell preparing for the proposals joked that they had to wear hardhats to protect themselves from the barrage of insults and cold shoulder treatment they received from their counterparts on the team. Eventually Sy realized he could not win against an IBM/Intermetrics team, and Rockwell withdrew from the software competition. Slowly we regained most of our status as a full Rockwell teammate, and he restored our logo on the public relations poster and other media material:

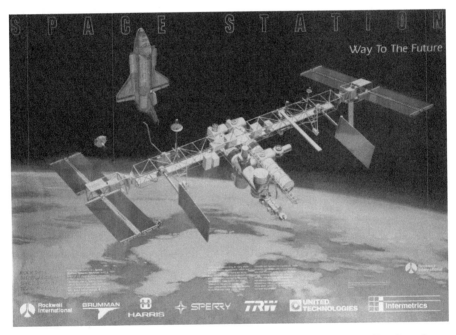

During this time, Sy contacted me to ask for a $500 contribution for a fundraising breakfast for an incumbent Senator from Michigan who was influential in approving funding for NASA programs. I was still naïve about these things. I called Saponaro to tell him I knew it would be good for Intermetrics to go along, but I had no intention of personally donating $500 for the reelection of a Democrat from another state. Joe told me to write the check and I would be reimbursed. When the reimbursement came by something other than normal payroll, I realized that this was probably illegal. I continued to get Christmas cards from the Senator for years afterward until he retired from the Senate. I concluded this thing was business as usual for congressional fundraising.

The competition for the Space Station software came a year before the prime competition for the ISS itself. It was a shock to the entire industry when NASA selected Lockheed over the IBM/Intermetrics team. When the IBM executives and I attended the NASA debriefing, we were entirely frustrated when NASA told us the competition was so close it "could have been decided with a coin toss!" NASA had made a major mistake with this selection. Over the next several years, after spending hundreds of millions of dollars, they gave up on Lockheed and awarded the contract sole source to IBM. Since IBM no longer needed Intermetrics to win, we got nothing out of it.

The competition for the prime Space Station contract was even worse. NASA selected the McDonnell Douglas Team based on a cost that was at least 25 percent below Rockwell's bid. Everyone knew the Space Station could not be built for the winning bid of six billion dollars. But NASA did not have the courage to expose this fact. The NASA I knew, who had the best managers and engineers in the Apollo era, had seemed to degrade throughout the Shuttle era. Now Space Station was being procured and managed by just another government bureaucracy who seemed unable to accomplish major objectives in manned spaceflight and wasted billions in the process. Today the Space Station is a fraction of the size of the winning design, was completed ten years late, and had overruns exceeding tens of billions! It was supposed to be completed and operational before the new millennium. Still, it is by far the largest object in space and a huge improvement over Russia's Mir space station. It is approximately the size of a football field and weighs 919,964 pounds.

NASA made another blunder in selecting Grumman over TRW to help them technically manage the development of the Space Station. A distinguishing feature of the Grumman proposal was that retired NASA people would manage their project. Seventeen of the top twenty-one proposed managers had been former NASA employees. Joe Saponaro actually helped Grumman win during the proposal phase with some Intermetrics employees from the East Coast, but received only a verbal assurance that we would get a subcontract for our efforts. It was never honored. Grumman quickly got into trouble because of the poor progress with the Lockheed and McDonnell Douglas contracts. I tried repeatedly to convince Grumman's President and Program Manager, Fred Haise (formerly the Apollo 13 Lunar Module Pilot) that we could help him save his billion-dollar contract, but he dragged his feet. This was another costly contract that was cancelled.

After the loss of Space Station, Sam Iacobellis replaced Sy's boss, George Jeffs, as President of Rockwell's aerospace sector. Iacobellis was promoted from President of the B-1 Bomber Division. Soon we learned that Sy was removed as President of Space Division. Sy was afflicted with narcolepsy, which causes a person to drop into instant deep sleep from a fully awake state. It was rumored that the reason for Sy's removal was that he had fallen asleep in the first row while the NASA director was speaking. But Iacobellis had a reputation for replacing all of his direct reports with his own choices. I was told that NASA management was quite unhappy with Sy's removal, although he was replaced by one of Sy's protégés, Bob Minor.

After Sy was out of power, a Rockwell VP, Bob Glaysher, announced that he was going to end our Shuttle contract and perform the Shuttle backup software builds for each mission in-house. This would have cut my total business revenue by 5 percent forcing layoffs at my Huntington Beach facility. Rockwell could have hired some of my experienced people and used them to perform the work. I scrambled to create a white paper, showing how only we were qualified to perform the work to NASA's and Rockwell's satisfaction and flight safety requirements, implying I would find other work to keep these people employed with Intermetrics if we lost the contract. It worked. Glaysher backed off and we continued the role until I left the company in 1993.

Sy was given one year to find another job outside of Rockwell, then was let go. At the suggestion of Saponaro, I hired him (at $1500/day) to consult for us on how to exploit our GPS experience commercially. I remember him having one of his narcolepsy attacks in the middle of a large strategy meeting. One minute he was talking, the next he was sound asleep. After a couple of minutes, he woke up and finished his thoughts almost as if there were no interruption. With Sy's help we came up with several good proposals, but Saponaro refused to fund them, or even to let us fund them ourselves using a fraction of our annual profits. Two years later, Sy was hired by McDonnell Douglas as a Senior VP, but he never had the success that he did with Rockwell in the Shuttle era.

Sy served on the NASA Return to Flight task group in 2005. He passed away in 2006.

31. *Columbia—Search for a Scapegoat*

At 6:15 AM on Saturday, February 1, 2003, long after I had retired from the business, I was awakened by a call from my sister, Kim, in Wisconsin, telling me to turn on the TV. NASA Mission Control in Houston had lost communication with *Columbia*, the oldest Shuttle Orbiter, as it began entry into the atmosphere from its sixteen-day mission in orbit, STS-107. It looked ominous.

Except for the OMS and small attitude-control jets, the orbiter has no power because the external tank, which provided the fuel during boost, was jettisoned during the launch phase. Entry had always been the most dangerous part of any space mission. There was a possibility of surviving even a booster-engine explosion on the launch pad, but no way for the crew to escape if something went wrong during reentry. The tremendous heat generated as the atmosphere slows the vehicle from orbital speed can be catastrophic. The ion field created around the vehicle during entry inhibits communications with the ground for a short period of time. The velocity and attitude of the orbiter must be precise as it encounters the beginning of the atmosphere approximately seventy-five miles from the earth's surface—so precise that the onboard computers, not the crew, control the spacecraft. The orbiter is traveling at 17,700 miles per hour in a free fall (coasting) trajectory. It aligns itself backward to its direction of motion and ignites its maneuvering thrusters to reduce the velocity by two hundred miles per hour. This changes its orbit from a near circle two hundred miles above the earth's surface to an ellipse in which the perigee (lowest point) is below forty miles altitude, causing reentry into the dense atmosphere. Then the onboard computer aligns the spacecraft perfectly; the bottom of the orbiter experiences the bulk of the tremendous drag. The heat-dissipating tiles on the underside absorb the resulting heat as the orbiter slows down. The heating of the tiles becomes increasingly more pronounced as the atmospheric

187

density increases. At the maximum deceleration, the crew experiences a force of only 3 Gs, compared to the 7 Gs during Apollo reentry. Orbiter's attitude at entry is critical. If the attitude is too high by even a fraction of a degree, the orbiter could skip off the atmosphere back into space. If too low, it would dig into the atmosphere, generating heat that would exceed the capability of the tiles to dissipate the energy in time, and the cabin heat would be too great to sustain life. In fact, the forces on the orbiter could cause it to break up. Only the onboard computers could steer the orbiter precisely enough to safely control this delicate balance. Even with perfect control, the temperature at the leading edge of the tiles exceeds 2,000 degrees Fahrenheit, while the cabin temperature rises only fifteen degrees. At approximately sixteen miles altitude, entry is complete. At this time, the orbiter acts more like an aircraft, in that the control surfaces (elevons and rudder) push against the atmosphere to utilize atmospheric lift and drag to control the attitude. But it is more like a heavy glider than a conventional aircraft, because it has no working main engine.

I recalled the controversy with the tiles during the final days of *Columbia*'s development and construction. Early tests in 1980 showed that the adhesive holding the tiles to the underside of the spacecraft was failing, and tiles by the hundreds were falling off. Rockwell put Sy Rubenstein in charge of fixing the problem. One of Sy's subordinates, Dan Brown, with whom I played golf at Mesa Verde Country Club, was the hands-on guy who directed a team of people to implement Sy's solution at the Cape. Dan was later promoted to Vice President at Rockwell. Although the major tile adhesive problem was fixed, damage to the tiles continued to be of concern throughout the history of the entire fleet of orbiters: *Enterprise* (which was never operational), *Columbia*, *Challenger*, *Discovery*, *Atlantis*, and *Endeavour*.

When I saw the multiple contrails of the *Columbia* on my TV screen, I knew that something had come off the orbiter and all was lost. If any significant part of *Columbia*'s heat shield of 24,300 unique tiles had been penetrated and burned through, the crew could not survive, even if the orbiter remained intact. I was horrified as I saw more and more contrails, indicating *Columbia* was breaking up. I couldn't help but think of the *Challenger* tragedy in 1986, which seemed like a short time ago. Even though I retired almost four years earlier and had no involvement with NASA programs since 1993, I still felt close to the Shuttle Program—a major part of my aerospace business for ten years.

But this *Columbia* catastrophe, as the *Challenger*, became media frenzy almost immediately. Just two days after the accident and twenty-four hours prior to the memorial for the seven Shuttle astronauts (even before all their remains had been found), the media had already filled their pages and the airwaves with finger-pointing commentary. The first target, of course, was NASA. Did they take too much risk? Were they too blasé about crew safety? Did they cut corners to keep the twenty-two-year-old *Columbia* flying? Had they diverted necessary Shuttle maintenance funding to their overrun Space Station Program? Had all their "good people" retired and been replaced by second-rate, inexperienced engineers and managers? Shouldn't the Shuttle Program be cancelled? It was easy for the media to now dig up comments over the years from whistle blowers who were eager to point these fingers. (I don't remember the media giving them this level of coverage when the program had its successes.)

A hole punctured in the leading edge on one of *Columbia*'s wings caused the accident, when a piece of insulating foam from the external fuel tank peeled off during the launch sixteen days earlier and struck the orbiter's left wing. The accusations by the media continued. Yes, there was a little truth in some of these accusations. The cost and schedule overruns in the Space Station Program had been enormous.

In 1987, when my Intermetrics team was a Rockwell subcontractor, Rockwell had lost our $8 billion bid for the development contract to build the Space Station to McDonnell Douglas by almost $2 billion. At that time the total program cost was budgeted at $8 billion for a space station much larger than the one being assembled today. As it turned out, the International Space Station's costs reached over $100 billion! Over the years NASA had significantly reduced the operational costs for Shuttle missions, and all of those savings have been diverted to Space Station (a mistake, in my opinion). It was also true that NASA has changed. In the Apollo era, both NASA and its contractors attracted the best and the brightest to push the last frontier: space. Eventually, these top people had retired or left the NASA programs; replaced mostly by engineers and managers who joined programs that no longer held the prestige and glamour of their predecessors. This grew progressively worse as Space Station overruns mounted with accompanying criticism.

But this new breed of aerospace engineers and managers may have been more risk averse, rather than risk takers as their predecessors. As in most government bureaucracies, taking a calculated risk and succeeding was not sufficiently rewarded, but being wrong could cost you your job. This was clear to me in the waning days of the Apollo Program, when we found several significant errors in the IBM software used for ground control of the missions and identified the obvious corrections. Yet, instead of authorizing these corrections, NASA management rewrote mission rules to either not use that part of the software or devised manual work arounds to correct the problem. And instead of giving congratulations for finding and reporting the problems, NASA buried the flaws, in order to avoid the embarrassment of drawing more attention to them.

This phenomenon grew worse during the Shuttle era of the 1980s. NASA paid Intermetrics over $3 million to develop a new compiler to replace the one we had developed in the 1970s. But neither NASA nor the IBM users had the courage to use it, fearing risk of the unknown. Instead they continued to use the old compiler with its known errors, avoiding the instructions which invoked the errors. In my opinion, this practice was becoming widespread ... illogical, and absurd to the knowledgeable outside observer. But it demonstrated how risk averse NASA and its contractors were becoming.

Once the news media realized that NASA need not be the only target for blame for the *Columbia* disaster, they quickly began attacking the politicians. After all, wasn't it Congress and the President who decided to cut NASA Shuttle funding? So, weren't they to blame for the risks introduced into the program by pressuring NASA into reducing the costs for each Shuttle mission? Enormous pressure built as Bill Clinton took office. The new NASA Administrator, Dan Goldin, came up with the "Faster, Better, Cheaper" NASA war cry. Shuttle budgets were cut repeatedly throughout the eight-year Clinton administration, and this practice did not change during the George W. Bush administration. Yes, this may have contributed to the safety problem. And the media pounced on it. Finally the politicians backed off from their stand that we have to control NASA costs, and promised to reinstate Shuttle maintenance money. If they really wanted to control costs, they would have killed the Space Station long before, but this would have taken political courage. In fact, without Space Station, it would be hard to justify extending the Shuttle. More than 75 percent of the Shuttle missions supported assembling and maintaining the Space Station. Although some things only astronauts can do in space—such as correcting satellite problems—there is an argument that many of the tasks can be done much cheaper robotically, without humans. NASA's JPL demonstrated real success with many of their robotic probes throughout the solar system. However, clearly Apollo 11 would have been a failure if Armstrong had not steered the *Eagle* clear of the boulders. And the Musgrave crew's success in correcting the Hubble Telescope's optics may have

191

been worth the price of the whole Shuttle Program. But, the safety factor necessary to "ensure" humans will return to earth safely is very expensive. Even in the Apollo era I remember the GM Vice President for engineering bemoaning how we unnecessarily had to design "human factors" into the guidance system, despite knowing that automating the functions would be more efficient, accurate, and cheaper. He called the demands by the Apollo astronauts to "push the buttons" the "Linus blanket syndrome," named after the Charlie Brown character who had to have his hands on his security blanket. I'm sure he had second thoughts when Armstrong had to maneuver the *Eagle* to avoid landing on a boulder to prevent mission failure. The politicians dared not eliminate the only programs requiring a man in space, but had no qualms about cutting the budget to the bone to maintain them. The Clinton Administration was of the same ilk, and Goldin knew what he had to do to keep his job as Administrator.

With the press pointing their fingers at all these candidates for scapegoat, the media have omitted blasting one other key segment of society: **the media itself!** The media have played a tremendous part in influencing how the politicians, NASA, and the public deal with the manned spaceflight programs. When Projects Mercury, Gemini, and Apollo were in their glamour days, the coverage was major and positive by all branches of the media. But once Apollo 11 landed on the moon, they—more than any other force—caused the glamour to change to skepticism, disillusionment, and apathy. The lines of print and air time concerning the Apollo 1 fire, the *Challenger* disaster, and the *Columbia* accident exceed the coverage of all the accomplishments over the past forty-two years of space exploration, with the possible exception of Apollo 11. Think about it. How much coverage have the media given the programs' accomplishments between the *Challenger* disaster in January 1986 and the final STS mission in 2011? How much did we know about this *Columbia* mission, STS-107, before the horrific footage of *Columbia*'s reentry?

The media is a contributor to our failures in space. They have spent forty-seven years harping on the dollars spent on the space program. I remember Walter Cronkite reciting the dollars per second spent on burning Saturn rocket fuel as Apollo 12 was lifting off. It was the news media who put the pressure on Congress to cut the Shuttle budget, berating the cost per pound of putting a Shuttle payload into space. Powerful network anchormen use their daily pulpits to 100 million Americans to influence Congress, the President, NASA, and the general public. Why do they do it? Not because they necessarily believe they are taking the right position for the nation. Rather because it attracts attention, sells papers and TV ads. It is the media, more than any other group, that I blame for the difficulty we have today in persuading our bright children to study math and science in order to pursue a career in the space field. This is why we do not have the caliber of professionals in the space field we had in the late 1960s. It is a vicious cycle: space has more problems than successes; space is no longer cool; cutbacks reduce opportunity for individuals; the best people seek jobs elsewhere; lesser talent introduces more errors and problems.

It would seem that only the astronaut corps continues to attract the best and the brightest. The attractiveness still remains with this small group partly because the media continue to portray them as brave heroes. At first, I was disappointed when my son decided not to become an astronaut. He was on the perfect path to becoming a pilot for the Shuttle:

- Distinguished Graduate from the Air Force Academy

- Majored in astronautical engineering (minor in Russian) with a 3.7 GPA

- Instructor pilot for the twin engine T-38 jet

193

- Grew up in the astronaut community near the Johnson Space Center and had a friend in BG Charlie Duke who walked on the moon

- Was continuing his career as an Air Force pilot

But as Scott and his wife began to raise a family, he decided not to apply. He did not want to put his family through a required tour as a test pilot at Edwards AFB, nor be away from his family for extended periods of time. Today I am happy he chose differently.

I am disappointed in the media's inaccuracies in covering the space programs; they never seem to acknowledge their errors or correct them. Of course, I am more sensitive to these bloopers than the general public. But I am incensed when they continue to broadcast wrong information, and then wonder why our children get science so wrong. Dan Rather gave a good example of this as he tried to describe reentry into the atmosphere. He said they were at 200 miles above the earth (It was 43 miles or 207,000 feet.), and traveling at six times the speed of sound. (It was 23 times.) I've never heard any significant coverage on space where they made these kinds of mistakes, yet ever correct them. I remember TV coverage of Apollo when NBC Anchorman Frank McGee tried to explain the orbital mechanics of rendezvous. He couldn't have messed it up any worse. His explanation broke Newton's Three Laws of Motion! I wrote him a three-page letter, politely explaining rendezvous correctly in layman terms. I did not receive a response to my letter, but at least he never tried to explain it again.

I don't think it has to be this way. The media doesn't have to be perfect, but they can admit their mistakes like the rest of the world who is under the public microscope. They have a duty to provide accurate information to the public, and then let the people make up their own minds on the value of the programs. They should not be spouting data that contradicts the laws of physics. If they don't know what they are talking about, they should find someone who does. And their bombardment with a perverse slant on the facts should not be influencing manned space policy and opinion for our nation.

32. *Fired!*

Okay, so officially I was "laid off," along with virtually all of my staff and my CA Division Manager. But the shock was the same as being fired. How could it happen? Especially to me? Wasn't my performance better than any other general manager in the company? Didn't I prove myself over a ten-year period? But there were signs. ...

Joe Saponaro hired me in 1983. At forty-three years old, Joe was clearly the rising star in the company. He had worked his way up from one of the first twenty employees of the company in 1970 to GM, VP, and Board Director by 1980. The performance of his group led the other groups in growth and profit margins. Joe was a smart man—a hard charging Italian-American from Boston, well-liked by customers and respected by his employees. He exhibited a keen sense of business savvy. Although a little rough around the edges and highly competitive, Joe had a sense of corporate politics, and could be a street fighter when necessary. He also worked on controlling a temper, which he usually held in check. Joe did have some weaknesses. In my opinion, he was too detail-oriented, lacked some communication skills, and not always a good judge of people until he really got to know them.

A year after I joined the company, Joe transferred to Intermetrics' Cambridge headquarters, as our new President. As the director of new business development for the past year, I had led our penetration into the new world of aerospace software required by the Department of Defense. In part, acknowledging this performance, but mainly based on my management experience, Joe appointed me his successor, "acting" GM of ASG. I had "arrived." At age forty-four, I had finally realized my career goal of moving up to GM of an engineering organization involved in the space and defense field. I now had bottom-line responsibility for all the operational aspects of an $8 million line of business and one hundred employees. Within six months, Joe had removed the "acting" qualifier on my title and given me a raise, stock options, and a new company car. Growth and profitability were key goals for the company. This was especially true for my Huntington Beach Division. The small Seattle and Huntsville offices had never shown a profit. Joe wanted me to close Huntsville and see if we could turn a profit in Seattle. But few of us foresaw the big picture looming:

- The Reagan build-up peaked;

- Defense growth soon ended;

- The Soviet Union collapsed;

- Cuts in both military and NASA spending began an annual norm (the Clinton "peace dividend");

- The large prime contractors subcontracted less, trying to keep more of the shrinking business in-house to minimize their layoffs;

- The many small engineering companies like Intermetrics and Ultrasystems either got swallowed up by acquisitions or went under.

But despite these adverse forces in the aerospace business, we met or exceeded most of our goals (at least for the next eight years). My salary and performance bonuses continued to climb. In my first full year as GM, the profits and cash flow of ASG actually saved the company. Our flagship organization in Cambridge had lost over $2 million on a series of firm-fixed-priced Ada compiler development contracts for the USAF and several computer manufacturers, including IBM. These losses would ultimately total $4 million over several years. The negative cash flow and the tarnished reputation of poor performance on these contracts could have easily sunk a public company of our size.

Fortunately we managed to achieve outstanding performance on my NASA and military contracts. In addition, I had closed our Huntsville office and sold the remainder of this business, making the first profit the office had seen since its opening five years earlier. We also turned around the Seattle office, making its first profitable year since its inception. As a result we generated a positive cash flow of $2 million/year, due primarily to a 15 percent profit on $8 million in revenues. Our quarterly meetings at corporate headquarters were gratifying. I loved my job! But Joe, now President and CEO, was under tremendous pressure from the Board of Directors and stockholders because of the poor company performance overall and the perpetual falling value of the stock. The profit and contract problems had now manifested themselves into a low growth rate in revenues. Joe closed down one group in Cambridge and replaced the GM of the software development group with a young technologist, with little success.

I acquired a perk in representing Intermetrics at the Air Force Space and Missile Division in El Segundo. The Commander of the Division (a three-star General) decided to hold quarterly meetings with all his prime contractors, inviting the CEO of each company. Since Saponaro did not want to attend, I went in his stead. So, I rubbed elbows with the top management of all the USAF giant contractors. One in particular, TRW's Dan Goldin, had been appointed NASA Administrator by George H. Bush in his last year as President. Dan succeeded Dick Truly, our former neighbor. When President Clinton took office, he retained Goldin as NASA Administrator, in part because Dan was a Democrat. I congratulated Dan, who first responded with a written thank you, then followed with this letter after he took office.

Goldin was the longest serving NASA Administrator serving three presidents.

NASA

National Aeronautics and
Space Administration

Washington, D.C.
20546

Office of the Administrator

August 1, 1992

Mr. Kurth Krause
General Manager
Intermetrics
5312 Bolsa Avenue
Huntington Beach, CA   92649-1090

Dear Mr. Krause:

After being on the job for four months, I finally have an
opportunity to thank you for your kind thoughts on my
appointment as NASA Administrator. I was so pleased to
receive your comments. The encouragement and support I have
received from everyone has been greatly appreciated.

I have achieved the ultimate fantasy of my career in
being appointed NASA Administrator and have never been
happier. Though the challenges are great, the satisfaction of
leading the United States civil space program is far greater.

We of the NASA team will continue to reach for the stars,
to make the world a better place in which to live, and to
provide opportunities for future generations.

Sincerely,

Daniel S. Goldin
Administrator

By 1992, we had grown ASG to $19 million in sales, 180 employees, and had delivered 63 percent of the company's aggregate profits over the past nine years. The stock options Saponaro awarded me each year, based on group performance, would have made me a wealthy man if only the company's stock had not shrunk in value over these eight years—from $16/share to $4/share. So I believed I was a shining star in a company which was in the doldrums. But there were signs.... I was not politically savvy, in fact a little naïve when it came to corporate politics. At our quarterly operations meetings in Cambridge I voiced my opinions openly, even when they conflicted with Joe's. I thought if my ideas had merit, this was the best thing to do for the company—to speak directly and freely. I thought it might even help counter a possible image that I was Joe's "yes-man." After all, I was the only GM hired directly by him. The others were hired by his predecessor and founder, John Miller, who remained Chairman of the Board. So I thought that occasionally expressing an opinion differing from Joe's would be healthy. When he forcefully countered my arguments, I thought it was just a part of the same healthy discussions and in keeping with his personality. In retrospect, he may have taken my disagreements as disloyalty or disrespect, but never told me so.

One of Intermetrics' five founders was Ed Copps, a brilliant, soft-spoken engineer who was then in his late 50s and on the Intermetrics Board of Directors. He had worked in an upper management position when he reported to Joe in Huntington Beach, but Ed's skills did not fit a management role. Since Ed wanted to remain in Orange County, Joe asked me to find a position for him in the Aerospace Systems Group. But Ed received an extremely high salary, making it difficult to find a customer willing to pay for it. Also my project managers did not have a role for his unique talents that would justify his compensation. After years of failing to find a proper role for Ed, I made the mistake of holding Joe to the promise that he would cover Ed's salary and benefits to relieve the burden on my group's overhead. Once again I gave little consideration to the politics—Ed being a member of the Board. Joe thought my complaints tactless, and never forgave me for treating Ed that way. Up to that time, Ed had always been my supporter, but afterward, may have had second thoughts.

By mid-1992 our growth had stopped. For the first time, I would miss my key goals. I told Joe our biggest problem in this recessionary and competitive aerospace climate came from our too high overhead. Our competitors were slashing prices to stay alive, and our customers demanding we do the same. Two large parts of our high overhead were our costly unoccupied space in the Huntington Beach facility (our lease still had two years to run) and our share of the allocation of Joe's corporate expenses. I had complained about this for several years, but Joe told me I would not be happy if he took action to fix the problem. In 1992, I told him it had to be fixed whether it made me happy or not. Our communication started to break down.

I had tried to fix the lease problem myself. As early as 1985, I could see we made too much of a commitment, and I convinced the landlord to relieve us of our additional 8,000 square-foot annex. Office space was in demand then, and he could easily find another tenant. We tried to sublease a part of the new facility, but security clearance requirements made this difficult. We tried to take advantage of a loophole in the contract to force the landlord to solve our problem, but Joe killed this approach. He thought it would be sleazy to do this to his landlord friends with whom he had done the original negotiations. The landlord offered to reduce the lease price per square foot to the now poor market price, provided we signed a new five-year contract. But this would be folly since we only needed half of the 25,000 square feet.

The one bright spot for 1992 was a big one. Despite our non-competitive rates, we won a five-year contract to continue to provide independent verification of the flight software for each Shuttle mission. This contract, worth $20 million, was, at the time, the largest ever awarded to Intermetrics, and it gave my group a record backlog for the coming years. But instead of Joe giving us the accolades we deserved for this key award, Joe said I was "lucky."

I also played a key role in winning the largest contract ever awarded to Intermetrics just a few months earlier. NASA in Washington, DC originally wanted to award an IV&V contract for the space station software to the loser of the Grumman and TRW competitors for the prime development software. This would, of course, exclude Intermetrics from winning the IV&V competition. But I convinced NASA that their plan would not work. The winner of the development contract would shut out their losing competitor because they would forever be a real threat to taking over if the prime contractor stumbled. This is exactly what TRW did to the independent contractor on our ballistic missile defense program. Only a small business that was not a threat to the prime contractor had a chance of being accepted into the program to independently test and verify the prime contractor's software. NASA bought my argument! Intermetrics competed and beat TRW in winning the $80 million IV&V contract for the space station software, but it would be performed by our East Coast division, rather than my ASG.

Perhaps ironically, Joe acknowledged my contributions to the company every year, resulting in generous raises which doubled my salary in eight years. He also awarded me bonuses and stock options each year, including a bonus of $40,000 each of the prior two years.

Joe expressed displeasure when I awarded a big bonus to John Hanaway, who was retiring. I believed John certainly deserved the bonus for bringing in the $20 million Shuttle contract. But Joe did not believe in rewarding someone who had announced his retirement and would no longer be contributing to Intermetrics goals.

As we began 1993, I had every indication something negative was in the planning. Joe's communication with me had stopped. He held meetings in Cambridge without me. My colleagues at the Southern California Technology Executives Network (SO/CAL/TEN) had warned me about these signs. Joe had stopped paying for my $4,000 annual membership dues. But I was in denial. How could Joe dismantle the Group that had generated 63 percent of the profits of the company and remove its leader? Certainly the board of directors would stop such action.

In late January I got a call from Joe's secretary that he was en route from Cambridge to meet with me in my office that afternoon. When he arrived he got right to it. He was folding my whole organization into the Warminster, Pennsylvania group that serves our US Navy contracts. I and most of my staff would be laid off immediately. The objective was to reduce the overhead to make us more competitive. Warminster would provide our human resources, contracts, pricing, marketing, and other administrative services. I would receive a severance package of 15-weeks' salary and an office at an outplacement center to find another job. He said he felt sorry to do this, since I had done so well for the company, but a business decision had to be made. Next, he had similar layoff meetings with the director of my California Division, my deputy for administration, my human resources manager, and my marketing director. He spared my contracts manager and the directors of my Seattle Division and my Houston Division, but within a year, all three were gone. Later, I learned that he had also replaced the technologist who ran the Cambridge software group with a member of the board of directors.

I was in shock! What would I do? This was the middle of the aerospace recession. From a peak of 273,000 employees in Southern California private aerospace companies, we had reached a low of 92,000. Clinton was in office, and military and NASA funding were low priorities. Should I try a different field? I remembered the last big aerospace recession in the early 1970s and the signs that read "Aerospace need not apply." But aerospace was all I knew! This recession could only get worse. How could I find a comparable job at age 52? Many of my colleagues from SO/CAL/TEN had been jobless for many months under similar circumstances. Some had given up looking. I was still too young and had insufficient savings to retire. Could I go back to a technical engineering job? Not likely at my age. I hadn't performed hands-on technical work in twenty years. But at least I had a support network. I knew I could get good references from Joe, John Miller, and my subordinates. SO/CAL/TEN would try to help. So would my personal network of customers, peers, and maybe even competitors. The outplacement center may help. Best of all, Sue would provide great support as always. (In fact, she took a refresher course in her chosen profession of occupational therapy and ultimately went back to work as a Registered OT.) But I knew it would be doubly difficult for me to find a good job, being out of work. People like to hire key people by stealing them from competitors, not from the street. I thought, *okay, it would be tough, but I can do it. I may have to give up my coveted perks: first-class travel, plush corner office, company car, stock options, bonus, six-figure salary, membership in Who's Who in America, SO/CAL/TEN membership, and colleagues at the top levels of companies, but I can do it. And I will be stronger for it.* "What doesn't kill you makes you stronger."

33. *Job Search—A Campaign*

There I was—January 1993, out of a job at age 52 in the worst aerospace recession in twenty years, with harder times coming. I hadn't been unemployed since starting work in 1963 right out of college. It would not be easy. I had to get my act together. No time to sit and feel sorry for myself. The day I was laid off, I reported to my outplacement office, which I decided to use to the fullest. The severance package entitled me to a small private office, secretarial service, use of their job search library, and advice from a full-time HR professional. The service would not get me a job or even leads, but would advise me on résumé writing, interviewing techniques, and general job hunting methodology. More importantly for me, I could use the advisor assigned to me as a sounding board in planning and implementing my job search. I bought an executive job search book, *Rites of Passage at $100,000+*. But first, I needed to reassess my severance package.

Had the company treated me fairly? After ten years with Intermetrics, with a good performance record as General Manager, did I deserve only fifteen weeks' severance pay and six months of outplacement service? I realized I could not receive this advice from the outplacement service, due to their conflict of interest. After all, their paying client, the CEO of Intermetrics, had just fired me. I called Jeff Weiss, one of the founders of SO/CAL/TEN, and he referred me to a lawyer who specialized in executive compensation. The lawyer advised me to negotiate hard with Joe. I knew I had no legal leverage, having no employment contract with Intermetrics, but I could appeal to Joe's sense of fair play. As an executive with full profit and loss responsibility, reporting directly to the CEO, I deserved more than this. Precedence in the industry gave executives special treatment when they were terminated, (sometimes called a "golden parachute").

I called Joe and arranged a meeting for the next morning, prior to his returning to Boston.

I decided to conduct the meeting on a business-like basis. Although I was appealing to his sense of fair play, I would present my case and tell him what I expected in a matter-of-fact approach. First, I pointed out my difficult position—trying to secure an equivalent job while unemployed. I requested Intermetrics to keep me on the payroll while I job hunted, allowing me to perform my search from a stronger position than from the rolls of the unemployed. Second, I requested keeping my basic benefits: medical, dental, and 401K until I found a new job. Third, fifteen weeks was insufficient time to find an equivalent new job. Executive job search statistics showed an average search time of one month for each $10,000 in salary, which meant it might take me a full year to find a comparable job, maybe longer in this recession. Finally, I wanted to exercise the Intermetrics stock options I had received and wanted Intermetrics to waive the hold on the restricted stock I had been awarded the previous year for my performance. Joe acknowledged that the major contribution I had made to Intermetrics deserved special consideration. He promised to review my requests and get back to me. But he added how it was important to him that, since the objective of this entire action was to save the company money, he would have to weigh my arguments against the costs to the company.

To my surprise, Saponaro came through! Applying the advice from the lawyer and the book worked. I would remain on the payroll, working out of the placement office for the first fifteen weeks until I found a new job. I would be guaranteed a total of six months' pay, even if I found a job sooner. I would receive my medical and dental benefits during this time. After six months, if I had not found a job, I would continue to receive salary and benefits for up to an additional six months, but the expensive outplacement service would stop after fifteen weeks. I could exercise the stock options previously granted, and the legend would be lifted on the restricted stock I had received. (Two years later, when Intermetrics was bought out by a private company, this became an important financial benefit.) The one stipulation: I was prohibited from disclosing the terms of this settlement. With the advice of my lawyer, I signed the agreement. Later I learned this agreement actually helped Joe make peace with the board of directors. He may have taken this bold layoff step and reorganization without consulting the board. I had supporters on the board, including Chairman John Miller, who may have not been very pleased with Joe's action to fire me. Joe actually added one more concession, which I had not asked for. Intermetrics continued to make the lease payments on my company car (a 1991 Chrysler Fifth Avenue) until May 1993. At that time I bought the car from the leasing company for the residual value.

With the finances and our economic security satisfied for the next twelve months, I was ready to devote my full attention to the job search. I was determined to treat it as a full time occupation. I stayed at the outplacement center every day from the time it opened at 8:00 AM until it closed at 5:00 PM. I dressed in my usual business attire: suit or sport coat, dress shirt and tie. This helped to provide the mindset I needed to work this role as diligently as I had in my previous job. I read several more books on executive job search and started to craft my résumé. Most importantly, I began to generate my list of people who might help—my network.

The résumé was a problem. I knew I could create an impressive one for an aerospace executive position, but were there any openings? Aerospace companies did need someone who could bring in new business during these lean times, but new business development was only part of my role, rather than a full-time responsibility. I could apply for a management position in another field, but why would someone hire me without experience in their field? With the exception of some commercial aircraft products and services for my Boeing customer, all my work had been for US military and NASA customers. I could apply for a non-management job in the aerospace field, scarce as they were, but I certainly wouldn't hire someone who had to take a significant salary cut due to the risk of them leaving as soon as they found a better position. In addition, my technical skills were rusty, not having performed hands-on technical work since I rose to second-level management in 1974. I decided to start with a basic, straightforward résumé based on my aerospace management experience, and then tailor it if I applied for a specific opening.

I first generated a list of accomplishments. This filled several pages and helped my bruised ego. Next I prioritized the list in order to pare it down to fit into a two-page résumé. Finally I fleshed out the boilerplate: education, chronological list of companies, job titles, and relevant associations. The hardest part was writing the Job Objective. If I focused it to a specific objective, I narrowly restricted my opportunities. If it were broad enough to cover a wide swath of positions, it sounded vague, implying I was not sure of what I wanted. I opted to use a summary profile, instead of the classical Position Objective.

Once I completed the résumé, I began the active phase, calling and/or writing to my contact list, applying for jobs listed in the Wall Street Journal and other publications, researching the companies and their executives, and sending my résumé with a cover letter to more than one hundred executive recruiting firms. The only recruiter I had ever hired (to find me a director of marketing a few years before) had retired. I contacted hundreds of customers, competitors, friends, everyone at my SO/CAL/TEN network, former employers, as well as their referrals. My best contact, my former boss—Jack Distaso at TRW— had recently been promoted to VP and General Manager of

TRW's largest division. But, due to the decline in business, he was in the process of laying off dozens of his direct reports, who were at the same level as I. I even contacted some of my former astronaut neighbors, most of whom I had not seen since our Houston days. Fred Haise (the Apollo 13 LM pilot) was then President of Grumman Technical Services and Program Manager for the Space Station support contract in Washington. But they were in performance trouble with NASA and cutting back.

I had not seen Bill Anders since he left the astronaut corps in 1969, after being one of the Apollo 8 crew in 1968. He was CEO and Chairman of the Board of General Dynamics, so I contacted him to see if he had anything available. But he had just reduced his staff by 80 percent and was in the process of selling off major portions of the company. He responded with this letter:

GENERAL DYNAMICS

3190 Fairview Park Drive
Falls Church, Virginia 22042-4523

William A. Anders
Chairman of the Board

703-876-3008

May 26, 1993

Mr. Kurth W. Krause
1918 Suva Circle
Costa Mesa, CA 92626

Dear Kurth,

Thanks for your letter of 17 May. Indeed, it has been a long time since Woodland Drive, El Lago. I've passed on the information about Scott to both my boys. Greg, by the way, is now a B-52 instructor pilot at Castle Air Force Base.

As I'm sure you're aware from press accounts, we've been restructuring quite significantly here at General Dynamics. Having just resigned as a company officer myself this month, I can assure you that GD is not in a hiring mode right now. In order to get our costs down for the efficient franchises that remain, the corporate headquarters, for example, will be downsizing from 250 to 50 people by the end of 1994. A consequence of having won the Cold War!

I'm not aware of any specific opportunities in our industry at present, but what I might suggest to you, Kurth, is that you give William (Bill) Tobin a call at Korn/Ferry International in Washington. He is always on the lookout for talented, experienced people in the defense sector. Bill can be reached at 202-822-9444. He's a great guy, and as you probably know, Korn/Ferry is one of the best in the business.

I hope everything goes well for you and the family.

Warmest regards,

William A. Anders

Two of his sons had attended the Air Force Academy while Scott was there. Months later, Bill retired from General Dynamics.

210

By May 1993, 4½ months after starting my search, I had filled three notebooks with contact plans, ads, follow-up letters, thank-you letters, cover letters, and notes taken at the handful of true job interviews to which I had been invited. None of these were a real fit for an aerospace manager with my background. The closest had been an opening for a marketing VP at Loral Librascope, a submarine manufacturing division of the former Ford Aerospace located north of Los Angeles, some sixty miles from my home. But, after the interview, the president told me I was more suited to take his job than become the marketing director. I realized he was right. Instead, they hired a colleague, whom I had once considered hiring as my director of marketing in the late 1980s.

I began to get discouraged. Did I need to look outside the Southern California area? We really didn't want to move. And who knew if there were any better opportunities in the rest of the country? John Miller suggested I apply to NASA. But that would mean not only moving to Washington or Houston, but dealing with the bureaucratic, slow-moving organization that NASA had become. I knew I would not be happy there. What if I couldn't find a good job?

I tallied our finances. Thanks to diligent investing, I had accumulated a pre-retirement nest egg that would generate approximately $25,000 per year in income until we became eligible for Social Security. Even if we dramatically cut back on our expenses, this would not be enough to sustain us until then. We now had an empty nest. Scott was an Air Force pilot; Sheryl had graduated from Cal Poly San Luis Obispo, and taught elementary school. Both had married and did not need our financial help. But I could not retire at fifty-two. Although Sue hadn't been employed since we started raising our family in 1965, she might be able to get a job in her occupational therapy profession where there was a shortage, but it would not be easy at age 53. I told myself this recession could not last forever, and it was just a matter of time so long as I kept at it and kept pursuing every possible lead.

I was down to the remotest contacts in my network list, when I caught a real break. I called Bob Richards, the president of Aerojet in Azusa, CA, whom I had met on two occasions. We had tried to pursue some new business together more than a year earlier without results. I barely knew him, but he remembered me. He told me Aerojet was looking for a senior manager to lead a new opportunity for developing a satellite ground station for a classified program for the US Air Force. Bob had just retired, but would set up an interview for me with Executive VP Dr. Phil Buckley and his subordinates. The next week I drove the forty-three miles to Azusa to meet with Buckley and his Directors: Marketing, Defense Support Program (DSP) support contracts, Software Development, and Human Resources. Although my knowledge of DSP was peripheral, it was sufficient to conduct stimulating interviews with each of the principals, and ask relevant questions. My last act before leaving Ultrasystems in 1983 had been to win a small contract with IBM Federal Systems to upgrade the DSP ground-station software. Aerojet now needed someone to lead the campaign to unseat this IBM incumbent for the DSP ground station to replace the current one in multiple locations around the world. From the feedback, I felt I was "in," and would receive an offer. But the Director of Ground Stations, a key decision maker was on a business trip. I scheduled another interview with him two weeks later. Armed with the salient information about the new business opportunity, my interview with Director Nick Gionis the following week went very well. In the meantime, I learned from another network contact that Aerojet had hired a search firm to fill this position, but after rejecting more than one hundred candidates, they were still looking. This put me in an excellent position for bargaining when they made me the offer two weeks later. Although they would not budge on the salary, which was $6,000 under my current salary, I was able to negotiate:

- A $25,000 sign-on bonus to be paid over two years,
- Immediate participation in their 401K plan,
- Severance pay of three months' salary if they were to lay me off for any reason other than "for cause,"
- An option to pay for my relocation if I decided to move closer to Azusa in the next two years.

However, as many aerospace companies, they were in a salary freeze that might last years. It certainly was a step down from General Manager—and not only a cut in salary, but also in bonus potential; and no stock options nor first class travel perks. But it was a challenging job and a chance to be a hero if I succeeded. After some sole searching, I accepted the offer.

By mid-June I was on board, and my job search ordeal was over ... or so I thought. ...

34. *Saving Aerojet*

When I was selected from one hundred other applicants to join Aerojet Electrosystems in Azusa, CA to lead their thrust into the satellite ground stations line of business, I did not realize the company needed saving. They had been producing the surveillance sensor payload for the USAF DSP satellites for twenty years, all sole source and highly profitable contracts.

DSP Satellite Monitors Earth for ICBM Launches

Their new Army contracts for SADDARM tank killers were promising. Their long-term solid rocket business in Sacramento seemed steady. Sure, they had just sold off the munitions and chemical business lines, but that allowed them to concentrate on the ones important to me: space and defense. They had made significant

214

technological inroads into IBM's twenty-year stranglehold on the USAF satellite ground station business with small wins for both Air Force and Army tactical ground stations. I saw this as a major growth opportunity—for Aerojet and my career.

But at the time I didn't recognize what I soon would believe to be their fatal flaws:

- An older, entrenched, top-heavy management looking to hang onto what they could until near-term retirement;
- A rigid hierarchical-management philosophy which did not delegate, reward, or encourage innovation from lower and middle management;
- An open-ended environmental cleanup problem from their rocket testing in their Sacramento headquarters that would be a continuing drain on their resources, thereby impacting their competitiveness.

Sure, there were signs I should have recognized from my interviews: managers who had stayed with the company their entire careers; no incentive bonus system at my level or even at the director level; bureaucratic decision-making; undisciplined software development processes.

But, perhaps unconsciously, I repressed these observations in favor of convincing myself that this was the best opportunity I could find in this recessionary aerospace industry. After all, it was spring of 1993. The Cold War was over. The Soviet Union had collapsed. And defense cutbacks were an acceptable way to reduce the deficit and thus mitigate some economic problems in the country.

It didn't take long for me to recognize the flaws. Almost the day I started at Aerojet, the USAF gave notice to both TRW (who built the DSP spacecraft and integrated the Aerojet payload) and Aerojet that they were canceling the next contract for the three DSP satellites currently on order at over $1 billion each. A new system of surveillance satellites, FEWS, would replace DSP. The current inventory of six DSPs not yet launched would sufficiently fill the gap until FEWS was built. This would mean almost 50 percent of the Azusa plant's business would evaporate, along with the vast majority of its profits. The layoffs would come, and Aerojet Azusa would die.

My next shock came in building the business model. The first time I got access to the proprietary bidding rates, I thought there must be a mistake. In order to cover their costs, Aerojet had to charge the government $250,000 per man-year of engineering labor, more than three times the annual salary. I knew facility costs required to build and test space payloads created a high overhead, but Aerojet's clearly was not competitive with the rest of industry. It would be devastating to the ground station business, where our competitors did not have the burden of covering expensive satellite payload manufacturing facility costs. When I presented this problem to the rest of management, some thought my numbers were wrong. VP- and director-level management apparently did not even know their own costs, let alone how they compared to their competitors. I drafted a proposal to segregate the ground systems business from the manufacturing, as so many competitors had done, to create a competitive cost structure, but it was ignored.

Another problem was their unused capacity. Aerojet had more than one million square feet of office space and nearly one hundred acres of land. Much of this was unnecessary for this now smaller company that could not begin to utilize it. They wanted to sell off some of it, or even sell the entire company, but the rocket-engine environmental cleanup liability prevented it. There was no way to truly estimate the cleanup cost. They did reach an agreement with the Department of Defense that the federal government would pick up two-thirds of the costs annually by adding it to the company's bloated overhead charges on their government contracts, and Aerojet would pay the other third out of profits. They attempted to estimate the total cleanup cost at $240 million, writing this off on the balance sheet, and reducing the company's net worth to less than zero! Of course the stock plummeted.

I thought it would have been smarter to separately sell the Aerojet contracts and personnel to an aerospace firm, while selling the buildings and land to a developer, who had experience in cleaning up environmental problems. But then no one asked me. I guess Aerojet didn't want to take the chance of unraveling the deal with the government to pay for two-thirds of the cleanup.

In 1994 John Yasinsky was hired from GE to become Chairman and CEO of GenCorp, Aerojet's parent corporation. He tried to sell the Aerojet Company. Bernie Schwartz, the CEO of Loral, who had been buying up mid-size aerospace companies, was interested. A team of Loral executives, technical lead engineers, and accountants were sent to our plant to perform due diligence in auditing our contracts and prospective new business to evaluate its worth. After some reluctance on our part to let our competitors in on our new business plans, Yasinsky ordered us to reveal all. Then, after a week of intensive auditing, we got a call from Sacramento to "give Loral nothing and show them the door." Next week I got a call from a friend who was president of a Loral division. He explained what happened. Schwartz had put a firm offer on the table, providing Aerojet would cap the cleanup liability. Yasinsky refused. Finally, after hours of negotiations, Schwartz said, "All right. I'll accept all liability and give you a buck for the company." Abrupt end to negotiations!

During the first few months I had also learned of alleged Aerojet violations of the Federal Acquisition Regulations in their efforts to

217

win a competition for an Army mobile ground station to process DSP sensor data to track tactical enemy missiles. The first was an alleged accounting violation. They had developed a prototype of the mobile ground station and charged the million-dollar cost to their overhead instead of capital (i.e., the government paid for it rather than the company). Then, in an effort to eliminate the only real competitor, they "gave" IBM Federal Systems a subcontract role on their bid team (a possible anti-trust violation). After they won the competition, the Aerojet corporate attorneys found out about the scheme and threatened to expose it. But a compromise was reached, and it blew over.

The problem of the uncompetitive overhead cost remained. A large share was due to their top-heavy management structure. In selling their munitions and chemical businesses, Aerojet had been reduced from four divisions to two, in Azusa and Sacramento. Both divisions were relatively autonomous, each with its own president and support staff. Yet there had been no reductions in the size of the Aerojet corporate structure in Sacramento that "presided over" these two independent divisions. This was now a company smaller than $1 billion in annual revenues with twenty-nine vice-presidents, each with his own staff. And what were the results of an off-site meeting of the VPs to reorganize into a new smaller company faced with high overhead, layoffs, and shrinking sales? A matrix organization with twenty-seven vice-presidents! When I first saw the new org chart, I honestly thought someone had created this as a joke. And the Aerojet "super-president" (Roger Ramsier) of this monstrosity actually had the nerve to claim this as their answer to needing a leaner, meaner, competitive company. Did he think his employees (and customers) were total morons?

It is no wonder then, that they didn't have the courage to make the necessary cost cutting measures that affected the employees directly.

For example, I was encouraged to take several in-house "prestigious" leadership-training courses, which were of no real value, especially to me, since I could teach these subjects in the real world. I was also allowed to take as many computer software courses as I wished to learn Microsoft Windows, Word, Excel, Power Point, and Project. My time for all this training was charged to overhead, further increasing our costs. They did freeze salaries for all employees, but dared not cut the costly benefit programs, such as health care and retirement.

So, in the midst of all these problems, how would I fulfill my goal of advancing my career by unseating IBM with Aerojet's approach to building ground stations for the USAF? I also learned, to Aerojet's surprise, that IBM Federal Systems Division had already presold the Air Force on upgrading their existing DSP ground stations with the next generation of giant IBM mainframe computers, the ES-9000 series. If contractually approved, IBM's lock on this business would continue for my lifetime, and Aerojet's ground station dreams would remain dreams. Should I give it up and look for another job? The best that Aerojet had going was some very talented, experienced engineers and a proven, elegant solution to a better ground station.

In late 1993 the aerospace job market was not getting better. I knew many of the key decision makers at TRW, thus making it the most logical prospective employer for me. But TRW was continuing to lay off engineers and offering early retirement to anyone over fifty. Divisions were being merged, eliminating 50 percent of the middle-management positions. Based on my network of industry contacts, opportunities at my level and age remained nil. Moreover, I could not stomach being a quitter. While I knew I did not want to work for Aerojet long term, I desperately wanted to leave with more accomplishments under my belt. I made up my mind to give it my all. I had to develop a new strategy to undermine IBM's solid position, while perfecting our alternative approach. We had to repudiate the

IBM solution, while convincing the Air Force at all levels that ours was the logical, low-cost, low-risk alternative. And it all had to be done despite our exorbitant overhead costs. By this time I knew that management lacked the courage to solve this problem. It would not be easy. The good news: Aerojet had excellent engineers.

TRW was well aware of IBM's jump on the next generation ground station, and they approached Aerojet with a joint plan to derail IBM's head start. Fortunately, The Government Accountability Office (GAO) had criticized the Air Force's intention to go with the next generation of IBM mainframes because of its cost and limitations. TRW knew that Aerojet's solution for a ground station for tracking tactical missile launches using the DSP sensors was superior to IBM's solution. During my first few weeks with Aerojet, the two companies built a briefing on why the TRW/Aerojet solution was superior. Although I was new and not at all up to speed on many of the technical problems and tradeoffs, my participation in the joint strategy was of immense value to me as a learning experience. And I enjoyed renewing acquaintances with some of my TRW colleagues. Aerojet resented having to let TRW take the lead, but they realized TRW had both the software reputation and the relationship with the Air Force customer that was lacking at Aerojet. Since I was the Program Manager for this initiative, I should have been the spokesman for Aerojet. But with my limited knowledge of DSP technology and only a few weeks with the company, it was decided that the presenters would be TRW's senior program manager and Aerojet's Director of Software. The latter had worked with the DSP Program almost his entire 30-plus years with Aerojet. I considered myself lucky that I was not responsible for the failed presentations. Although the technical arguments for the TRW/Aerojet solution were superior to IBM's, the risk and politics had not been presold to the Air Force.

The meeting was a disaster. The TRW and Aerojet VPs involved with the program were present, together with an audience of nearly thirty people. Our team's two speakers were shot down in flames by the Air Force DSP Program Manager. He was clearly worried about the risk of going with a new computer and new software instead of the incumbent, IBM. When the ashes had settled, TRW was out of the picture, Aerojet senior management wanted to distance themselves from the embarrassing fiasco, and the Senior VP who hired me, Phil Buckley, declared it was my program to save. Although I would get less support, it was now clear that I was in charge ... at least so I thought.

Armed with the elements of the technical approach and the knowledge of the risks and politics pressuring the Air Force customer, and with the help of some experienced, talented Aerojet engineers, I started to create a series of briefings:

1. Why the IBM approach is high risk, not low risk. Why the old software must be redesigned to correct for the upcoming millennium turnover due to the poor IBM design. Why the IBM ES-9000 computers are limiting future growth and improvement, and do not accommodate modern technology graphics. Why the maintenance costs will remain high, yet replacements will still be necessary as new requirements evolve.

2. Why the Aerojet solution with modern, high-graphic computers is moderate risk. How it fixes the millennium (Y2K) rollover problem.[7] How it leaves room for evolution to accommodate new requirements.

---

[7]When IBM wrote the software, they assumed it would never be used beyond 1999, creating errors in hundreds of places when the year 2000 occurred.

3. How the Aerojet tactical system will easily accommodate the strategic objective of rapidly detecting and accurately tracking ICBMs.

4. Why it will be so much cheaper to integrate the tactical and strategic ground stations into a single system, not only for DSP, but also its successor.

5. Why data from actual DSP-detected launches demonstrate the viability of the proposed Aerojet system.

With the help of an Aerojet colleague, senior systems engineer Dick Rawcliffe, I began presenting the briefings to all interested parties in the Air Force, both at the Space and Missile Systems Division and at the Pentagon. It was a long shot, because we had to overturn the decision made by the Air Force Space Surveillance Program Office without alienating them. (The Program Office develops and produces the satellite and ground systems for the user command.) Our first success came from briefing the users of the current DSP system, who would also be the users of the new system to replace DSP—the unified Space Command (SPACECOM). Most of them liked what we presented. We appealed to the ease of using the new graphics compared to the archaic IBM displays, and to the low cost of maintaining the new system  compared to what they paid IBM to maintain the current system. They also were impressed with our integration process and transition from DSP to its replacement, satellite by satellite, as each is launched and certified on line in orbit.

Our next task was to convince the Air Staff at the Pentagon, who is responsible for getting the funding approved. After briefing the captains, majors, and lt. colonels dedicated to the program, we caught a break. One of the influential full colonels invited us in to give our presentation. We gave it everything we had, discussing each of the points in our five focused briefings. He became our champion and all but ordered the Program Office to listen to us with an open mind. With his help, we succeeded in killing the IBM solution. But the main decision makers would still come from the Program Office. Although we never did win all of them over, we did persuade the Program Office to hold a competition, rather than giving the ground station upgrade program to IBM sole-source. But now the stakes were much higher. The FEWS Program was cancelled, and a new $multibillion program—Space-Based Infrared System (SBIRS) —would be competed. It would contain the upgrades to the current ground station, the new ground station, and the new satellites to replace DSP. It would be the winner-takes-all Space Defense System for the next twenty years. The competition came in two steps: first to select two finalists, then a shootout for the big prize. The teams started to form.

Because the word spread on the success of our briefings, all three Prime Contractors wanted us on their team despite our high costs. I thought I would be a real hero for bringing Aerojet back from the ashes. But I was wrong. The politics at Aerojet had changed. The new Division President, Carl Fisher, had forced the ex-Executive VP (Phil Buckley) and ex-Senior VP (both of whom had hired me) out of the company. So I had two new bosses, Fisher and my direct boss, Director Nick Gionis. Now that Aerojet was back in the industry's good graces for SBIRS, they effectively pushed me aside to call all the shots. Since Grumman wanted to build the payload sensor, their interests lay only in Aerojet's ground systems capability. Therefore Fisher spurned Grumman's interests, and decided to leverage our ground station prowess with both the Hughes/TRW and the

Lockheed/IBM teams to see if he could get a piece of the satellite sensor work in addition to the ground station role. Hughes appeared to have a lock on the sensor because they had one with similar characteristics in operation for a highly classified program. Much earlier, they had agreed to be the sensor supplier for the Lockheed team. Therefore getting much of the sensor work for Aerojet would prove difficult. But Fisher must have realized this was the only hope for Aerojet to stay in the payload business.

Gionis asked me to be the proposal manager and collocate at Lockheed in Sunnyvale as they began to get ready for the proposal. Meanwhile, Fisher negotiated with both Hughes/TRW and Lockheed, playing both ends against the middle. I felt very uncomfortable while Lockheed management revealed their strategy to me. Their plan was to offer the low-risk solution, with an already proven Hughes sensor and the only two contractors with proven DSP ground station experience (IBM and Aerojet). When Lockheed found out Fisher was playing games, they gave me the cold shoulder, yet my bosses expected me to stay at Lockheed while the negotiation games played out. I requested we end this charade, and returned home. Ultimately Lockheed, who was having trouble with Hughes on the payload, agreed to give Aerojet a piece of the sensor. We returned to Lockheed with the full team. But Gionis would now be Proposal Manager. He would run things during the weekdays, while I was supposed to be the lead on the weekends. I refused and, instead, volunteered to work up at Sunnyvale Monday through Friday each week for the required three months, going home on weekends. By this time, I realized I had no future with this company, so I would no longer sacrifice my weekends to appease these managers.

I did my best to get Aerojet back into the ground station portions of the Lockheed proposal. In our absence, IBM had taken the lead in this area. One by one, I persuaded each of the volume captains to allow me to author portions of the seven volumes of the proposal, eventually giving Aerojet equal status with IBM. But my management did not appreciate this. Fisher only cared about the payload, and Gionis was still unhappy because I would not stay in Sunnyvale over the weekends.

Meanwhile, the rift with Hughes continued. We proposed the Hughes payload even though Hughes never showed up on the proposal team. They had teamed with TRW and were competing against us. Ultimately, the proposal was submitted with Hughes named as a "supplier" rather than a teammate. This made the Lockheed proposal quite suspect and risky. The third team, led by Grumman, had a Grumman payload sensor but no experienced ground station contractor. The three proposals were submitted.

The first stage of the competition was to award two winners with $80 million, 10.5-month competitive contracts to develop the final designs, based on the Air Force specific requirements. But it was rumored during the evaluation period that the Hughes/TRW proposal had overrun their page allocation, forcing the Air Force to not even consider the last pages of their proposal, eliminating much of the management section. Lockheed received several Air Force queries, asking questions about the payload supplier. The industry joke was that Hughes had no management, Grumman had no ground station, and Lockheed ... no payload! Lockheed actually tried to file a protest with the Air Force, claiming Hughes had violated a teaming agreement, but the Air Force correctly threw it back in Lockheed's lap, noting that this was Lockheed's problem, not the government's problem. Lockheed dropped the protest.

Grumman was eliminated, so Hughes/TRW and Lockheed/IBM/ Aerojet each won the $80 million contracts to generate competing preliminary designs of the space-ground systems. Subsequently the

Air Force would select the winner for the $2 billion SBIRS contract. This would include the development and delivery of the satellite and ground station replacements for DSP, transitioning from one system to the other over the five-year period when it would operate as a DSP/SBIRS hybrid. It would be one of the most important competitions in the history of military space.

However, clearly I would not play a major part so long as I stayed with Aerojet. While we waited for the start of the competitive contract, I was not a part of the planning or preparatory activities. Logically I should resign and try to join the Hughes/TRW team, where I would be highly welcomed, but I realized that I could not do so. It would look like I was taking all of Aerojet's trade secrets and selling them to their competitor at the most critical stage of the competition. But I also realized that Aerojet could not afford to keep me around doing nothing with my six-figure salary. I waited for the layoff notice!

Sure enough, it came. Gionis told me I would not be the Ground Station Program Manager (which was the job I was hired to do) because I had not taken enough of a leadership role (refused to work the weekends at San Jose?) and did not know enough about the details of the DSP sensor. He was giving me a two-week layoff notice. When I asked him what he thought of what I had done in overturning the IBM position and getting Aerojet back into the program, he tried to make the claim that they would have moved into that position without all my effort. Fisher admitted he didn't understand why Gionis had made these decisions, but was not about to undermine them. The New Business Development Director, Shelly Friedman, was incensed when he returned from vacation to learn I had been given the boot. Shelly was certainly aware of what I had accomplished in the twenty-one months since I joined the company, and was worried Aerojet may have jeopardized their opportunity on SBIRS.

I could not have been happier. They had now solved my problem, and I was free to pursue a job with the Hughes/TRW team because I had been laid off, rather than resigned. Moreover, they had to pay me seventeen weeks' severance pay per my hiring agreement, which was a shock to both Gionis and Fisher, who had not been involved in my hiring negotiations. Months later, when they learned that TRW had hired me to lead the key ground station role, they became frantic. Of course, I was prohibited from providing any Aerojet, IBM, or Lockheed proprietary data, but I sure knew what we had to do to catch up in the ground station competition.

Aerojet complained to TRW about my hiring. They warned TRW not to hire any more of their "key personnel." I was finally getting the recognition from Aerojet for the role I had played in their rise from the ashes ... but not in the manner I had originally expected.

35. *Burnout*

I accepted the offer to return to TRW in August of 1995. I had no idea at the time how this assignment would be a defining moment in my career and my life. I had left TRW after eleven and one-half years in May 1979 to find my fortune with a smaller company. Now I was back with a 150 percent increase in salary (from 1979), but a cut from my Intermetrics and Aerojet compensation. In fact, it was my lowest salary since 1989. My responsibility would be greater than I had when I left in 1979, but less than the general manager and program manager roles at Intermetrics and Aerojet. The big monetary incentive came with the fact that TRW agreed to bridge my retirement, counting my earlier service as if it were continuous. If I would stay long enough to replace the five highest consecutive salary years with my new salary, my retirement pension would increase eight-fold. In addition, I could get medical benefits generally offered only to people who retired from current TRW employment. My other incentive was the opportunity to beat Aerojet out of the new Air Force SBIRS competition. I felt both grateful and bitter that the new Aerojet executive management had laid me off after I had succeeded in getting them back into the race for the multi-billion-dollar program. Although again holding the title of Program Manager, I was actually a deputy to Earl Jones, my former competitor and peer.

SBIRS was the Air force's new program to provide the surveillance necessary to detect tactical and ballistic missiles launched from anywhere in the world. SBIRS was to track them, determine their launch sites, and identify their targets in sufficient time to warn and possibly target anti-missile weapons to destroy them before reaching their objectives. It also had classified objectives. SBIRS would consist of six high-altitude satellites and up to twenty-four low-orbit satellites, all with infrared sensors. The sensors would relay their data to each other and to ground relay stations that, in turn, would relay the data to a central Continental US (CONUS) ground station (GS). This GS would integrate and reduce the sensor data, identify the threat, compute its trajectory, and send the results to the National Command Authority and the four key user communities: the Unified Space Command, the Ballistic Missile Defense Command, the Strategic Command (STRATCOM), and the intelligence community for immediate action. In a nuclear attack on CONUS by land-based ballistic missiles, they had to be destroyed within twenty minutes—sooner for submarine-based launches and tactical missiles. Multiple levels of security prevent me from providing details of these missions and the required capabilities of SBIRS. The GS would also command, control, and position the satellites and the sensors.

SBIRS was designated the "eyes" of the defense against missile attack against the United States, a component of the Strategic Defense Initiative or "Star Wars" system introduced during the Reagan Administration. It was also to replace the Defense Support Program, the system of sensors on satellites that orbited the earth 22,300 miles high in circular orbits at the equator. Their orbital period was exactly equal to the earth's rotation, thus they appeared to be "stationary" over a particular point on the earth's equator. The Air Force Space Command controls these satellites, positioning them above strategic spots along the equator and "hot spots" during conflicts, such as the Gulf War against Iraq in 1991. The DSP system had served to detect and track strategic missile launches since its first deployment during the peak of the cold war in the 1970s. As such, it served as a deterrent and early warning system against Soviet attack. Only this early warning enabled the US sufficient time to launch a counter attack should the USSR launch a first strike. Without this warning, they could have attacked and destroyed most of our retaliatory missiles before they ever left our missile silos. Since the USSR ground station knew we had this "spy-in-the-sky" system, they realized we could and would retaliate before their first missile reached CONUS ... the basis of the deterrent. But DSP, only marginally effective in tracking tactical missiles—such as the Iraqi Scuds—and expensive ($1.2 billion per satellite), also contained old technology, both in space and on the ground. The ground-station software in the old IBM mainframe computers had to be replaced before 2000, since 115,000 assembly language instructions would malfunction due to the year-2000 problem (Y2K). The new SBIRS GS would have the capability of processing the DSP sensor data, and controlling the DSP satellites as the first step of deployment. Then, as they launched the new SBIRS satellites (or "birds," as the operational military called them), the SBIRS GS would process and integrate the data from the combination of DSP and SBIRS birds until all the DSP satellites were decommissioned.

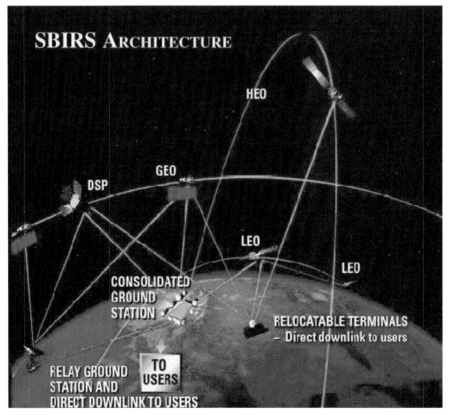

The Hughes/TRW team and the Lockheed/Aerojet teams had competed and each won 10 ½ month-long, $80 million contracts to design the SBIRS High System, consisting of the six-satellite Space Segment and the entire Ground Segment. (A separate contract for the design of the twenty-four-satellite SBIRS Low Space Segment was being competed later between a TRW/Hughes team and a Boeing/Lockheed team.) Hughes, as prime contractor, was in charge of designing the spacecraft and sensors, and integrating the entire system. TRW was in charge of the Ground Segment and providing the systems engineering. Earl Jones was Ground Segment Program Manager. I had the responsibility for the design of the CONUS GS, which accounted for 80 percent of the Ground Segment budget, staff, and capability. However, since Hughes had responsibility for the sensors, they would also provide the design of the sensor processing software in the GS computers. Therefore, they had control of most of my GS budget and 100 of the 120 employees reporting to me. I did not directly control the Hughes GS budget because it was embedded in the prime contract. Only the TRW budget was directly in our subcontract. The situation was awkward and unusual in that I had total responsibility for the GS performance, but controlled only twenty percent of its budget. This made my job more difficult.

My job was crucial to our strategy to beat the competition. Hughes believed because of their proven sensor they had the winning Space Segment. Based on feedback from the Air Force at the time, it was certainly favored over Aerojet's unproven paper design. But the Lockheed team had the clear advantage in the Ground Segment. They had on their team both incumbents, Aerojet and IBM, who had built the DSP ground stations. When I was with Aerojet I had convinced the Air Force that the Aerojet DSP tactical ground station, Talon Shield, was the right starting point to evolve into the new SBIRS GS. It would start with the existing DSP software for tactical threats, add the strategic threats, and then add the signal processing and command-and-control software necessary for the new SBIRS birds. Moreover, this was the low-risk solution, since the new GS had to replace the current strategic DSP system before Y2K, which was less than thirty-nine months away.

So the Hughes/TRW strategy was to close the GS advantage enjoyed by the competition and beat them in space. The focus was on my role. My strategy was to duplicate the solution I had already proposed for Aerojet. The issue: Could we convince the Air Force that we had learned enough about the Aerojet solution in just ten months and build it in thirty-nine months? We designed a program to demonstrate exactly that. We would build a prototype, starting with the Air Force-owned Aerojet software, and demonstrate it by processing the actual DSP data in real time. Many thought it an impossibility to do this successfully in such a short time. The Lockheed/Aerojet team was counting on it. The race was on! I didn't realize what a commitment this would take, or its toll on my lifestyle.

My team for the ground station and support equipment consisted of one hundred twenty talented TRW and Hughes software and systems engineers. My boss, Earl Jones—a smart, experienced man with unlimited energy—expected top performance from each of us. He knew this is what it would take to win. We all started working sixty-hour weeks, collocated at Hughes in El Segundo, some thirty-five miles from Costa Mesa. We had to brief our USAF customer every few weeks. Their GS lead, a Lt. Col. was every bit as energetic and competent as Jones. Action items for me (and my team) came in the form of emails, usually sent overnight from Jones, who, in turn, had received related information and action items from his USAF counterpart. I became the lead briefer when one of my lead programmers demonstrated fear of the task. Jones wanted to fire her from my team, but I convinced him that we needed her technical skills and could get by without her briefing the customer. She was ready to quit until I assured her that she would not have to brief again. We also supported joint meetings between the Lockheed/IBM/Aerojet team and the customer. Nick Gionis had taken my place on the opposing team and was surprised to learn I was now his counterpart on the Hughes/TRW team.

I had another talented lead programmer who reveled in being onstage. But he was looking forward to leaving SBIRS to work on a commercial satellite project for another part of TRW, as soon as they received the funding from TRW headquarters. I could not afford to lose him. I bypassed his Program Manager and went straight to the TRW VP, with whom I had worked, years earlier. But no luck. He said, since TRW was investing their own money in this commercial multi-satellite program, it was even more important than our multibillion-dollar SBIRS Program and they needed my programmer. But, then I got lucky. Their TRW funding wasn't approved until after our proposal was due, ten months later.

Our sixty-hour workweeks became eighty, then one hundred hours for the last two months before the proposal was due. We were exhausted, but did everything the customer expected and more. The proposals were submitted, and we waited, answering their insightful questions on our proposal. We promised the moon, to win. When the dust had cleared, we lost! We received perfect grades on the ground system, scoring higher grades than Aerojet/IBM, but lost it in the more important space segment. Hughes' abundance of confidence with their existing sensors had priced it higher than Lockheed did. Lockheed made amazing concessions to mitigate the risk of their new sensors and satellites. They volunteered to accept no fee (profit) until their satellites and sensors had been proven operational. (The winning Lockheed team ultimately encountered cost overruns of 25 percent.) I received several small bonuses from TRW for our GS performance.

At first I felt bummed that we lost. I had devoted ten months of my life to winning. But then I realized, had we won, we would have had to continue to put in long, stressful hours over the next five years to deliver what we had promised. (SBIRS ultimately ran into major cost and schedule problems with the GS software.)

For the first time in my life, I decided it wasn't worth it. **I had a life to live**. I began planning for retirement. To retire comfortably, I had to work at TRW until July 1, 1999 in order to maximize the TRW pension. I had always saved the maximum allowed for my 401k account throughout my career, and I had increased my savings for retirement ever since I left Intermetrics. But I needed the TRW pension, which I could elect to take as a lump sum, to meet my retirement goals. So now the desire to work hard and be a superstar took second place to maintaining my salary for the next thirty-nine months.

36. *Fighting Terrorism*

It could be argued that TRW was a pioneer in combating terrorism, based on our work on my final career project. In June of 1997 terrorists bombed the Khobar Towers building in Dhahran, Saudi Arabia, killing nineteen US servicemen and wounding 250 others. This, like so many other attacks on US interests, made it clear—long before 9-11—that our security was inadequate. Days after the bombing, TRW received a call from the Air Force asking how soon

we could produce and deploy the Tactical Automated Security System (TASS) —an air base intrusion detection system that we had been proposing for the past two years. By October, we were under a $47 million contract to install multiple systems to US military bases in Kuwait, Saudi Arabia, and United Arab

Emirates. Within 104 days, we rolled out the first truckload of equipment heading for Southwest Asia to protect our troops from terrorist attack.

TASS was to be my final professional project. By this time, I was burned out from the stress and long hours required to stay at the top of my management career. I was just looking for an eight-to-five job (or at most 7:30 to 6:30) for the next two years, and to save enough money to retire early before my fifty-ninth birthday. Although I would prefer the job to be interesting and challenging, the burning desire to be the best was now a distant second to transitioning to a full life outside of work. No longer would I put my life on hold to work the long hours to beat the competition and advance my career. Although TASS was far from the state-of-the-art space programs in which I had immersed myself through the years, it did offer the satisfaction of filling a critical need to protect our USAF deployments in the Middle East. Plus the project was to be performed in TRW's Dominguez Hills facility, seven miles closer to my home. Thus my commute time would be reduced by at least twenty minutes each way, compared to traveling the full thirty-three miles up the 405 Freeway to our main campus in Redondo Beach. It would be a step down in responsibility, as I would be a Deputy Program Manager, but that fit well with my desire to reduce the stress and time commitment for my final two years before retirement. So without letting anyone know of my retirement plans, I applied for the transfer and was accepted.

Although I was allowed to keep my official TRW title of Program Manager, denoting my senior status and pay grade, my role was to be the Systems Engineer for "Team TASS," for which I was not really qualified. I had not performed any hands-on engineering work in twenty-two years. My résumé described numerous management and business development accomplishments, with only one paragraph devoted to my early engineering achievements. Moreover, my engineering expertise was in unique space systems, not land-based perimeter security surveillance systems. But, with my math and physics education, the technology was not difficult to learn (not "rocket science"). The role was more one of management than technical innovation.

My first job was to take charge of the management volume of the formal proposal required by the Air Force before we were put under contract. This was easy for me, having been in charge of dozens of proposals in the past. We began the work of producing the system well before submitting the proposal in order to meet the immediate need for early deployment. This meant we took the risk of expending TRW money for the equipment and labor, in anticipation that we would be reimbursed after we were under contract.

TASS was to be comprised of off-the-shelf equipment, purchased by TRW from the manufacturers and vendors, and integrated with our computer software into a complete surveillance system. It would identify any intruder entering into an air base hosting our military, and alarm the intrusion to airman, soldiers, or marines sitting at a console. The equipment included a variety of passive and active infrared, seismic, and microwave tactical sensors, operating on battery, solar, or electrical power—plus the laptop and desktop computers in the central surveillance post. It also included the radio communication equipment required to integrate the system for rapid response to intrusions and hand-held sensors used by troops investigating the perimeter breach.

An intruder coming through the perimeter of the military base, where TASS is installed, sets off a radio frequency that is carried back to a desktop computer at the command post, illuminating an alarm on a computerized map of the base. Then the security police are dispatched in a Humvee to the location on the map, using their hand-held sensor to track any further movements, and radioing back to the command post. The TASS wide-area surveillance thermal imagery cameras can identify a human-size object up to one mile away and a vehicle from a distance of three miles. The thermal imagers also operate at night and during inclement weather. One problem arises when a false alarm is created by a wandering animal breaking the beam between sensors or sets off the trip wire. This technology is applicable to border security, but I don't know whether it is or will be deployed along the US/Mexico border.

After we delivered and installed TASS at the critical bases in southwest Asia, the military decided to enable the system for installation at bases all over the world including some domestic facilities. The Air Force held a competition for a much larger follow-on contract worth up to $495 million for these upgraded TASS systems. We had to make all our data available to our competitors, but we won the re-competition. I was The Technical and Management Volume Captain for the winning proposal.

As my last role on TASS before retiring July 1, 1999, I lead the redesign and upgrade of the TASS software. I personally wrote the Software Requirements Document, and then managed the software engineers who implemented the many software changes. That document lives today as the specification baseline for any changes to TASS. It received accolades from our Air Force customer, who expressed disappointment when they learned of my retirement.

TASS, of course, has limited application in the war on terrorism. It cannot be deployed in cities, or in places where crowds of people are free to come and go. TASS cannot be used to combat the attacks in the Middle East today, nor could it have prevented 9-11. It did a good job for what it was designed to do: protect perimeters of large, open-spaced bases. I was proud of my role in this project and what it *did* accomplish. To date, I know of no breaches of TASS security resulting in catastrophes, which are too well known in the world today.

But I don't miss the work. Since I retired, I never looked back; I'm enjoying my retirement too much to have any regrets. In fact, I wonder how I ever had time to work. When TRW asked me to come back for a while to help develop new business, I never even considered it. I did, however, have many dreams (nightmares?) about work. I must have been under more stress than I realized because these dreams—including those of TASS—continued over fifteen years, though their frequency has diminished significantly. I have returned to TRW on occasion to visit friends and attend retirement parties. I do enjoy people telling me how important and valuable my work was. But I don't miss those days for a minute. If anything, I feel relief that I am no longer under that daily stress. As I told my colleagues at my retirement party, "I have started my thirty year vacation." And without the stress, it might last much longer.

Epilog

When Bill Clinton became President, he announced that due to the "peace dividend" resulting from the end of the cold war with the Soviet Union, America would be downsizing our military. He suggested that companies doing defense business consolidate via mergers. This has come to pass, big time. The GM division (with which I started my career) downsized and is now part of Raytheon. The MIT/IL was divested from MIT and is now Draper Labs. Ultrasystems was decimated, and what remained was bought by Hadson. Intermetrics, which spun off from MIT/IL before the first lunar landing, was bought out by a video game developer, Looking Glass Studios. Aerojet in Azusa, CA is still in existence, but a small fraction of its size when I worked there. TRW, after buying BDM for $1 billion, was acquired by Northrop Grumman for $7.8 billion. NASA has downsized since Apollo. Like the DOD, its programs take too long and waste big money to accomplish objectives. (Some JPL space probes may be an exception, although half of them failed.)

I may sound bitter about all this, but I am not. I owe a great career to the opportunities created in the space environment. I have not met anyone who had involvement in Apollo and not named it as the highlight of his or her career. It certainly was mine. Perhaps this is because the technology was new; the funding at that time not an issue; and it attracted the best and the brightest dedicated young engineers and managers, enabling minimal management oversight and waste. I am concerned that unless our government entities get leaner and encourage more risk, we may not see an equivalent program again. I hope private entrepreneurs, such as Elon Musk with SpaceX and Richard Branson with Virgin Galactic, will be given the freedom to achieve their lofty objectives. I wish them well and yearn for my grandchildren to experience some of the luster of our ventures into this final frontier.

Recently I was on a cruise where a Smithsonian speaker gave a series of lectures on space. Lawrence Kuznets, a retired NASA engineer, is a published space author, who was responsible for designing spacesuits for the astronauts. Because of our similar backgrounds, I called him to compare experiences at JSC in the '60s and '70s. I told him I'd unfortunately missed his first lecture. He insisted that I attend his next one and sit in the front row. After his lecture on how he tried unsuccessfully to save the shuttle orbiters from being retired, he introduced me to his audience of several hundred people. He presented a bit of my Apollo software achievements, and told his audience I "was his hero." I have to admit that I enjoyed the applause, and for the rest of the cruise I was a celebrity—people stopping me in the halls and wanting to shake my hand. It was fun.

Acronyms and Abbreviations

ABM	anti-ballistic missile
AFA	Air Force Academy
AFB	Air Force Base
APL	Applied Physics Laboratory
ASG	Aerospace Systems Group
BBS	Badger Boys State
BG	Brigadier General
BS	bachelor of science degree
CAPCOM	capsule communicator
CEO	Chief Executive Officer
CIA	Central Intelligence Agency
CM	command module
Col.	Colonel in the USAF
CONUS	continental United States
CSDL	Charles Stark Draper Laboratory
CSM	command and service module
DIA	Defense Intelligence Agency
DM	Department Manager
DOD	Department of Defense
DOI	descent orbit insertion
DSP	Defense Support Program (surveillance satellite)
Dyna-Soar	Dynamic Soarer (X-20)
EDS	Emergency Detection System
ERNO	German prime contractor for Spacelab
ESA	European Space Agency
EVA	extravehicular activity (outside the spacecraft)
FEWS	Follow-on Early Warning System
FIDO	flight dynamics officer
FPS	feet per second
GAO	Government Accountability Office
GD	General Dynamics
GE	General Electric
GM	General Manager
	General Motors
GPA	grade-point average
GPS	Global Positioning System
Gs	acceleration forces measured in units of gravity on earth
GS	ground station for satellite control
GSOP	Guidance System Operations Plan

GUIDO	guidance officer
HAL	a modern high-order programming language, named after Hal Lanning, the MIT professor who invented it
HEO	high earth orbit
HR	human resources
ICBM	intercontinental ballistic missile
Ike	President Dwight Eisenhower
IMU	inertial measurement unit
IPO	initial public offering
ISS	International Space Station
IV&V	independent verification and validation
JPL	NASA Jet Propulsion Laboratory
JSC	NASA Johnson Space Center
KSC	NASA Kennedy Space Center
LEO	low earth orbit
LM	lunar module
Lt. Col.	Lieutenant Colonel in the USAF
LTV	Ling-Temco-Vought
MASCONs	mass concentrations (irregular densities of lunar mass)
MBA	Master of Business Administration
MDAC	McDonnell Douglas Corporation
MIT	Massachusetts Institute of Technology
MIT/IL	MIT Instrumentation Laboratory
MOCR	mission operations control room
MOL	Manned Orbiting Laboratory
MPH	miles per hour
MS	master of science degree
MSC	NASA Manned Space Center (later changed to JSC)
MSFC	NASA Marshall Spaceflight Center
NASA	National Aeronautics and Space Administration
NFL	National Football League
NRO	National Reconnaissance Office
NSA	National Security Agency
OMS	orbital maneuvering system
OT	Occupational Therapist
PC	personal computer
P&L	corporation profit and loss
PSQ	Personnel Security Questionnaire
RAM	computer random access memory
RCS	reaction control system
RETRO	retrofire officer

ROM   computer read-only memory
RV   reentry vehicle (nuclear warhead)
S1-B   Saturn booster used for low earth orbit manned launches
SBIRS   Space-Based Infrared System
SCIF   Specially Compartmented Information Facility
SDI   Strategic Defense Initiative
S-IVB   re-startable third stage of Saturn launch vehicle
SO/CAL/TEN   Southern California Technology Executives Network
SRM   Solid Rocket Motor
STL   Space Technology Laboratories
STRATCOM   US Strategic Command
STS   Space Shuttle Transportation System
TASS   Tactical Automated Security System
UCLA   University of California at Los Angeles
UFO   unidentified flying object ("flying saucer")
USAF   United States Air Force
US   United States
USSR   Union of Soviet Socialist Republics (Soviet Union)
UW   University of Wisconsin
VAB   Vehicle Assembly Building
WPM   Work Package Manager
Y2K   Year 2000

CPSIA information can be obtained
at www.ICGtesting.com
Printed in the USA
FSOW04n2312020217
30151FS